101 Uses for Your A/E Microcomputer

By Dan Raker & Rolland Thompson

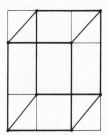

Design & Systems Research Publishing Company, Inc.
Cambridge, Massachusetts

101 USES FOR YOUR A/E MICROCOMPUTER

Practical Ideas for Everyday Situations
In Architectural and Engineering Firms

By Dan Raker and Rolland Thompson

Published by:

Design & Systems Research Publishing Company, Inc.
P. O. Box 1022
Cambridge, Mass. 02140, U. S. A.

First Edition, 1986

Printed in the United States of America

Library of Congress Cataloging-in-Publication Data
Raker, Daniel.
    101 uses for your A/E microcomputer.

    Bibliography: p.
    Includes index.
    1. Engineering--Data processing. 2. Architecture--
Data processing. 3. Computer-aided design.
I. Thompson, Rolland D., 1921-   . II. Title.
III. Title: One hundred one uses for your A/E micro-
computer. IV. One hundred and one uses for your A/E
microcomputer.
TA345.R35 1986   720'.28'5516   86-11670
ISBN 0-934605-00-9

Cover design by Randy Rumpf

Printed by Murray Printing Company Westford, Mass.

Editor's Note

Editors don't have the opportunity in the modern era
to study new technologies. They have few uses for
computers. Of course, they use them for word
processing. But how many editors know about
spreadsheets, databases or computer-aided design?
The task of assembling this book afforded me -- a
former Luddite -- with the rare opportunity to learn
about all of these computer tools.

With encouragement from the authors, I used these tools
during 90 percent of the work on this book. Databases
served as the watchdog for the indexing of the 101
ideas and ancillary information. Spreadsheets gave
credence to budget considerations. MicroCAD played
graphic designer. Of course, word processing -- the
most powerful tool ever created for editors -- aided
the writing and printing of the text.

I finished this project feeling very "macho" about my
new-found computer knowledge. I, therefore, thank the
authors who opened up this wonderfully intricate world
to me. In a strange, humanistic way, I also would like
to thank the various computers and software packages
that cooperated long enough to complete the book. I
still remain a skeptic.

In addition, I would like to thank Carolyn Colbert of
Design & Systems Research Publishing Co., Inc., who
helped with editing. Carolyn also offered solace
during some of the darker moments of editing. I also
thank Dodie Captiva, who set up and kept a meticulous
master file for all the examples in this book, and
Margaret Aiello, who lent her creativity to the layout.

-- Thomas H. Friedman, Editor

Acknowledgements

The authors would like to thank the many people and companies who supported the creation of the book: Amy Webster Thompson, Irving L. Levett, Chad Rider and Louis DiPaolo. These people listened carefully and advised during the book's early days and into the final hours.

People contributing their thoughts and computer printouts to be used as examples include: Todd Lee and Felicia Clark of Todd Lee/FR Clark & Associates; Frank Mascia of Collaborative Design Group; Christopher Doktor and Robert Stickles of the Architects & Associated Designers Inc.; David Arnold of D. C. A. Engineering, Inc.; Barthe A. Hague and LeRoy Troyer of The Troyer Group; Alan J. Krol and Edgar Galson of Galson & Galson consulting engineers; Douglas Clark and Jim Fraser of J. Kenneth Fraser & Associates; Jeff Berg of Berg/Howland; Dennis Lucas, Bill Abely and Nancy Oelschlegel of Computer Controls Corporation; Robert C. Robicsek of environ inc.; and the Denver Chapter of the American Institute of Architects. The Old South Church of Boston and the West Concord Union Church of Concord, Massachusetts are two institutions that graciously opened their architectural files to this project.

The authors would also like to express their gratitude to Autodesk, Inc. and Houston Instrument, which provided equipment for book production, and the MicroCAD Institute staff, which offered technical expertise.

Preface

The goal of this book is to make the design professional aware of the commonly found software packages that are easily adapted for the specific needs of the architectural and engineering community. The book does not offer ways to program your microcomputer or teach you how to use that software -- but instead provides "ideas" about applications of the software.

Those who have discovered the value of word processing will find in this book more hints about that software. The book also delves into the number crunching capabilities of spreadsheets, database processing and management, and the drawing power of computer-aided design. From this book, you will learn how powerful software packages are and how many applications exist beyond the advertised ones.

This book was written specifically for A/E's. Start with the table of contents, where every idea has been ordered based on aspects of office management or phases of project management. Office management is divided into marketing, personnel, accounting and general. Project management consists of the following phases: IA (pre-design), IB (schematics), II (design development), III (contract documents), IV (Bidding), V (Construction), and VI (post-construction)

This format means if you understand A/E practices, you aren't stymied by your level of computer literacy. The book is divided into sections based on software. Each section of the book starts with a description of the software and is filled with clearly written ideas. Examples supplement the ideas.

Finally, the book was created primarily on microcomputers and is itself an example of how the machines serve as a publishing tool. From thumbing through it, you will gain an appreciation for the power of general, off-the-shelf programs.

Table of Contents

Word Processing

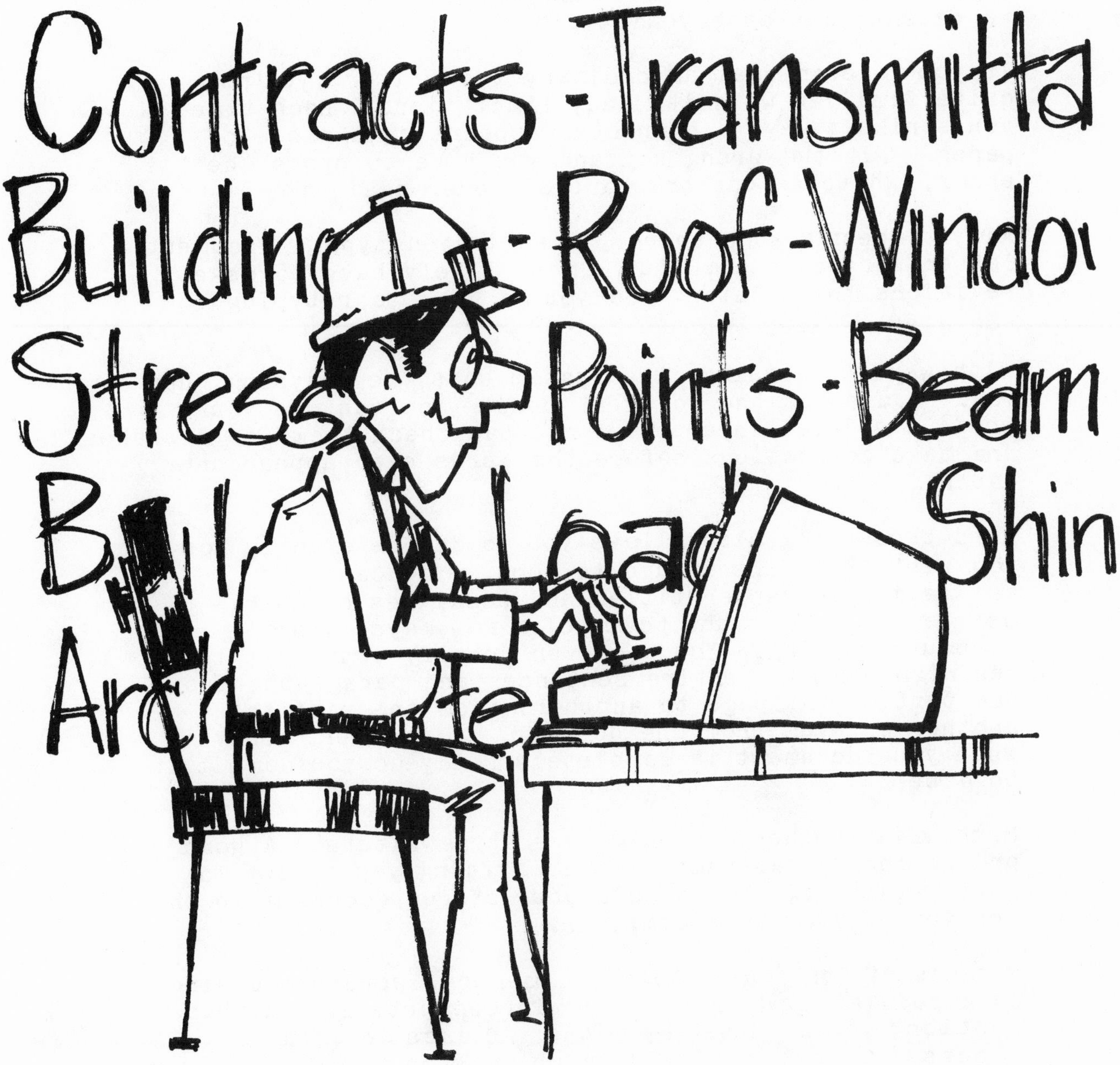

Word processing is a better, more efficient way to type. But it's much more than that: word processing represents a step beyond typing.

If you've ever used an ordinary typewriter, you're quite familiar with its many limitations. Each time you strike a key, a character appears on a piece of paper. Hit the wrong key and you have to erase the error, white it out or start all over again.

And it doesn't stop there. Even if you type a document letter-perfect once, you'll most likely have to make revisions to it later. So you're back to retyping it again anyway.

With word processing, the system does the retyping, not you. You enter the document once. You can see your words displayed on a screen and can check them for mistakes and make corrections before the words ever appear on paper.

Word processing also allows you to decide exactly how you want the printed page to look. You can automatically center titles and headlines or change margins -- all at the touch of a few keys, and all without retyping. You can even justify your text to the right or move entire sentences and paragraphs from one part of the page to another, from one page to another or even from one document to another. Only when your document is completely ready do you commit it to paper.

Memory is another advantage over typewriters. A word processing system remembers everything you type. To make revisions, simply call your stored document to the monitor of your microcomputer.

Because of its versatility and memory, word processing is a popular application for microcomputers. In this section, you will see more than 20 uses of word processing that you can do right now on a microcomputer.

1 Author Your Own Resume

No one finds resume writing easy. It requires patient self-analysis of your work history, weighing positive aspects against negative aspects. Resume writing has been known to set back the best of proposal authors. It creates writer's block for the most scrutinizing of authors and endless editing for the most boastful.

The word processor allows you to format your resume and your associates' to put your best foot forward. When you are preparing a resume for a proposal, order your information so that the most relevant is at the top. Move the block on hospital jobs from the bottom of the resume to the top of your accomplishment section for a hospital job. Alternatively, if you are bidding for a college chapel job, and you attended that college, then put your educational background at the top.

(Authors' Note: Keep a notebook of the latest resumes on hardcopy. The notebook will also serve as a handy reference when selecting associates for a particular job or for editing.)

RESUME	ROLLAND D. THOMPSON, FAIA	49 Beacon Street
		Boston, MA 02108
		1 (617) 723-3624

EDUCATION	Massachusetts Institute of Technology	MS, Engr '49
	Harvard Graduate School of Design	M Arch '48
	Harvard College	BS '43

PROFESSIONAL EXPERIENCE

Rolland D. Thompson, FAIA	Systems Consultant	Dec '79 – To date
Gruzen & Partners, (#1)	Architects	May '63 – Dec '78
Rolland D. Thompson, AIA	Architect	Jul '61 – Apr '63
Steinhardt & Thompson,	Architects	Sep '53 – Jun '61
Marcel Breuer (et al) (#2)	Architects	Jan '47 – Jun '53

Mr. Thompson, a practicing architect since 1952, has a career in master planning, programming, design, and construction administration of institutional, laboratory, higher educational facilities, religious, and residential work.

1978-1985

Since 1978, Mr. Thompson has operated as a systems manager and consultant to architectural and engineering firms, advising on management, and on manual and computer methods and systems of production, as well as CADD (computer-aided design and drafting). This work was accomplished through his consulting firm of "Design and Construction Procedures", and more recently through the Cambridge, Massachusetts consulting firm of "Design & Systems Research, Inc." in the field of CADD. He also advises firms on Construction Contract Administration.

He has consulted with Todd Lee/F. R. Clark and Associates, Inc., since 1982. The consultation includes project management, contract negotiations, production technology, use of micro processors in design, drafting, production, and accounting. He set up an office manual for standard details and administration of construction. He is currently associate with this firm on a number of projects

1963-1978

He served as project architect for the Pavilions of Spain and American Express at the '64/64 New York World's Fair. As Project Director for scientific and educational facilities, he directed and administered design, production, and construction of planning and building projects at the State University of New York at Stony Brook. These included the '76 updating of the comprehensive Campus Plan, detailed development of the Physical Sciences Area Master Plan, Earth & Space Sciences building, 2036 units of student housing in two separate dormitory projects, the Graduate Physics/Mathematics building, Social and Behavioral Sciences building, and Science Lecture Hall center; totalling at the time, more than $80 million of construction, most of which won awards for architectural excellence. He also completed the design and working drawings for the $52 million phase I development of the core campus of CUNY's recently completed York College in Jamaica, Queens.

1949-1963

As a general partner of Steinhardt & Thompson, he planned commercial, educational, industrial, and residential facilities. He was with the office of Marcel Breuer for 6 years where he participated in the planning of dormitory facilities at Vassar College and served as project architect for the Sarah Lawrence College Arts Center. With the organization of Breuer-Nervi-Zehrfuss, he spent a year in Paris engaged in the design stage planning of the UNESCO Building.

TEACHING

Mr. Thompson has taught architectural design at Pratt Institute in Brooklyn, construction technology at Columbia University's Architectural School, professional practice and management at CUNY's Architectural School and at the Harvard School of Design.

2 Packaging Consultants' Resumes

A/E firms hire others -- landscape
architects, mechanical engineers, civil
engineers, specification writers and
estimators -- on a project-by-project
basis. The job of maintaining information
on consultants requires careful management
of resumes. This practice expedites
proposal preparation and prevents A/E's
under the gun from mistakenly describing
consultants' qualifications.

Keeping up-to-date resumes -- that are
formatted like yours and ready for rapid-
fire inclusion in RFP's -- will greatly
simplify life. It also speeds up the RFP
preparation and delivery, eliminating a
last minute panic caused by geographic
separation between you and the
consultants, among other problems.

(Authors' Note: When you enter your
consultant's resume into your
microcomputer, you'll learn a lot. It's
good marketing to know as much as possible
about your consultants. Their expertise
and client connections could help you win
a job.)

RESUME   JORGE M. ROMANO, Principal, Romano/Erickson, Inc.   469 Franklin Street
                                                                       Cambridge,MA 02135
                                                                       (617) 661-2030

EDUCATION   Harvard Graduate School of Design   M Arch '79
            University of Pennsylvania   BA, Arch and Fine Arts '72

PROFESSIONAL Romano/Erickson, Cambridge, Massachusets   1985 - present
EXPERIENCE   Jorge M. Romano, Architect and Lighting Designer, Cambridge, MA   1979 - 1985
              Green Light Associates, Inc. Lighting Consultants Cambridge, MA   1978 - 1983

            Mr. Romano has been practicing independently since 1979, with his practice equally
            divided between architecture and lighting design. Among his lighting projects with
            Green Light Associates are the following representative projects:

                Big Bend Art Museum, Big Bend, TX
                V. R. Schmidt and Associates, architect
                Design/testing of natural lighting; lighting layouts and details for galleries,
                offices, auditorium, outdoor exhibit spaces, parking and fountains

                Crystal Tower, Boise, ID
                George Dyles, architect and developer
                Natural and artificial lighting for converting hotel to offices & shopping mall.

                Government Service Veterans System Headquarters, Indonesia
                7/11 Architects, design architect
                Development and testing of natural and artificial lighting with models and full
                scale mockup. Artificial lighting design and review of contract documents for an
                auditorium, gymnasium, and exhibit area as well as site lighting. Project won
                Lighting Industry Energy Conscious Design Award.

                Roger Williams Library Addition, Western Rhode Island University, RI
                Ten Associates, architects
                Schematic lighting layouts and details

            Harley Davidson/Graphics, Cambridge, MA
            In-house architect/graphic designer (part time).   1976 - 1977

            Charles Chaplin and Associates, Architects, Newton, MA
            Drafting/design development, residential projects (part time)   1976 - 1977

TEACHING   Graphic School of Design, Providence, RI
            Adjunct Faculty, Division of Architectural Studies
            Co-Lecturer for "Acoustics and Lighting".   1982 - present

            James Hancock College, Danbury, CN
            Adjunct Faculty, Architectural Division
            Co-Lecturer for "Acoustics and Lighting".   1982 - present

ASSOCIATIONS American Institute of Architects
              American Solar Energy Society
              Designers' Lighting Forum

PUBLICATIONS Harvard Architecture Review, Associate Editor

AWARDS   Designers' Lighting Association, Hartford; Lighting Fixture Design Competition, 1st
            Award, Professional Division, 1986

3 Conquer 254/255

The average citizen faces government forms
only at tax time. And are they glad when
they've dropped those tax forms in Uncle
Sam's blue postal boxes. Unfortunately,
A/E's who do government work or work for
large bureaucratic institutions are
required to fill out 254/255 forms.

If you pride yourself in beating the
government, you'll love this idea. Input
a 254/255 into your word processing
software or design your own to supply the
same information. When you need to use
the form, fill in the blanks ONLY. Yes,
you don't have to do anything else.
Moreover, if you put in for the same kind
of project all the time, then you won't
have much editing.

Architects & Associated Designers Inc. of
Boston, Massachusetts has such a form.
The firm provides this example:

<table>
<tr><td rowspan="3">STANDARD
FORM (SF)

254

Architects-Engineer
and Related Services
Questionnaire</td><td colspan="2">1. Firm Name/Business Address:</td><td>2. Year Present
   Firm Established:</td><td>3. Date
   Prepared:</td></tr>
<tr><td colspan="2"></td><td colspan="2">4. Specify type of ownership:</td></tr>
<tr><td>1a. Submittal is for

☐ Parent Company ☐ Branch or Subsidiary Company</td><td></td><td colspan="2">☐ A. Small Business
☐ B. Small Disadvantaged Business
☐ C. Woman-owned Business</td></tr>
</table>

5. Name of Parent Company, if any:	5a. Former Parent Company Name(s), if any, and Year(s) Established

6. Names of not more than Two Principals to Contact: Title/Telephone

1) _____

2) _____

7. Present Offices: City/State/Telephone/No. Personnel Each Office   7a. Total Personnel ☐

8. Personnel by Discipline: (list each person only once, by primary function.)

☐ Administrative	☐ Electrical Engineers	☐ Oceanographers			
☐ Architects	☐ Estimators	☐ Planners: Urban/Regional			
☐ Chemical Engineers	☐ Geologists	☐ Sanitary Engineers			
☐ Civil Engineers	☐ Hydrologists	☐ Soils Engineers			
☐ Construction Inspectors	1 Interior Designers	☐ Specification Writers			
1 Draftsmen	1 Landscape Architects	☐ Structural Engineers			
☐ Ecologists	☐ Mechanical Engineers	☐ Surveyors			
☐ Economists	☐ Mining Engineers	☐ Transportation Engineers			

9. Summary of Professional Services Fees Received: (Insert index number)

Last 5 Years (most recent year first)

	19__	19__	19__	19__	19__
Direct Federal contract work, including overseas					
All other domestic work					
All other foreign work*					

*Firms interested in foreign work, but without such experience, check here: ☐

Ranges of Professional Services Fees

INDEX:
1. – $100,000
2. $100-250,000
3. $250-500,000
4. $500-1 million
5. $1-2 million
6. $2-5 million
7. $5-10 million
8. $10 million +

101 Uses For Your A/E Microcomputer

4 Create Your Own ENR

We live in an information society. Television is no longer dominated by networks, but have additional cable channels. Magazines are not for leisurely Sunday reading. They are essential parts of business. Newspapers -- once rumored to be dying -- are in the midst of a resurgence. Why? We live in a society where information stimulates us.

Despite the rise of these forms of media, one of the fastest during the past ten years has been newsletters. They are the small organization's best means to reach its audience. With a newsletter you have power -- and moreover, you have the power to control the message.

With a microcomputer and a letter quality printer, A/E's can become a newsletter publisher. If you want to typeset a newsletter, you merely have to hand over a disk with files to a type shop. It cuts the cost -- and decreases turnaround time.

Galson & Galson consulting engineers of East Syracuse, New York publishes a regular newsletter. This is what it looks like:

The GALSON RECORD

Vol. 2, Iss.5

2/17/86

G&G MARKETING NEWS

by Russ Dionne, G&G Vice-President

G&G has been short listed for 5 major air conditioning projects with the Facilities Development Corporation (a NYS agency). Projects range from $10M to $40M in construction value. Our goal is to be selected for any one of the projects, and our ambition is to win the largest project. With competition the likes of Syska and Hennessy, EBASCO, Metcalf and Eddy, and many other big-name firms, we may be dreaming. But we will give it our all-out effort. Our best asset is our success on the St. Lawrence Psychiatric Center Boiler Project.

RESOURCE RECOVERY PROJECT

by Lee Davis and Peter Pohlot, Air Quality Department

The GTS meteorological department recently completed a flow characterization study for a proposed 500 ton per day resource recovery facility. We were hired to perform an in-depth study identifying and characterizing potential adverse atmospheric flow conditions resulting from a nearby 400 to 500 foot high ridge at one of the three proposed sites. In addition, we also determined minimum stack height necessary to avoid any adverse flow conditions.

The study considered two types of adverse flow conditions that are likely to occur in a valley situation and that would possibly result in increased ground-level concentrations of pollutants.

Our investigation focused on a review of available literature of previously performed field and fluid modeling studies of terrain similiar to this site and a detailed review of three months of meteorological data collected from an on-site Doppler acoustical radar (SODAR).

Reproduced below are two examples of the graphics generated inhouse for this report:

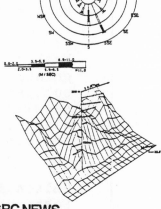

GRC NEWS

by Karen Munze, GRC Secretary

A patent on a slurry process to dehalogenate soil contaminants will issue on March 4, 1986.

5 End RFP Despair

Requests for Proposals consume time like no other piece of paperwork. It's not so much finding consultants to pack into your proposal, looking for kudos, proposing a delivery schedule or selecting references.

The problem isn't even how to pick a strategy. You're experienced and knowledgeable about that. The issue is simply: how do you compile a well organized and readable document to meet a bid deadline?

Leave the organizational tasks to word processing. Keep every pearl of information from other RFP's in files, carefully indexed. Don't be surprised if you use a whole disk. RFP writing is now a matter of adding information to files and editing.

4. OWNERSHIP AND USE OF DOCUMENTS. Drawings, renderings, specifications, and other documents produced by the Architect under this Agreement, as instruments of service, are and shall remain the property of the Architect, provided that upon payment of amounts due the Architect hereunder, the owner may retain copies, including reproducible copies, for information and reference in connection with the Owner's use and occupancy of the Project. Under no circumstances shall the Owner elaborate, change, or incorporate such documents into documents prepared by anyone other than the Architect, or permit such elaboration, change, or incorporation without the Architect's written consent.

5. ARBITRATION. All claims, disputes, and other matters in question arising out of or relating to this Agreement or the breach thereof shall be decided by arbitration in accordance with the Construction Industry Arbitration Rules of the American Arbitration Association then obtaining unless the parties mutually agree otherwise. This agreement to arbitrate shall be specifically enforceable under the prevailing arbitration law. Any demand for arbitration shall be made within a reasonable time after the claim, dispute, or other matter in question has arisen, provided that in no event shall such demand be made after the date when the institution of legal or equitable proceedings based upon such claim, dispute, or other matter in question would be barred by the applicable statute of limitations. Any arbitration hereunder shall be held in Boston, Massachusetts unless the parties agree otherwise. The award rendered by the arbitrators shall be final, and judgment may be entered upon it in accordance with applicable law in any court having jurisdiction.

6. TERMINATION. This Agreement may be terminated by either party in case of substantial breach by the other, upon seven days written notice. In the event of termination not the fault of the Architect, the Architect shall be compensated for all services performed to the termination date, together with reimbursable expenses, which shall include all damages (including, where applicable, lost profits) provided for under applicable law.

7. ESTIMATES. Since the Architect has no control over construction costs or contractors prices, any construction cost estimates are made on the basis of the Architect's experience and judgment as a design professional, but the Architect cannot and does not warrant or guarantee that contractors' proposals, bids, or costs will not vary from the Architect's estimates.

8. OWNER'S RESPONSIBILITIES. The Owner shall furnish such legal, accounting, and insurance counseling services as may be required for the Project and shall provide the Architect with all existing information relating to the Project which the Architect

PAGE 2 OF 3

On-Line Office Manual

No in-house document befuddles A/E firms more than the office policy manual. It requires indepth study of human issues rather than conceptualizing a design. A/E strengths are in design and not personnel.

Here's another ideal application for your microcomputer: No, microcomputers don't have the intelligence to write your office policy manual. But microcomputers do have the memory capacity and editing capabilities to retain your office policy manual. They also make it easy to update and print out.

(Authors' Note: Expect a meteoric rise in office morale. Employees like to have policy manuals. It makes them more secure about their rights and the firm's expectations. They will also like your capacity to incorporate their brilliant gripes into a new section of the manual.)

The **Denver AIA** chapter supplies an example:

6.16   PROFESSIONAL LICENSING AND CERTIFICATION

ALL EDITING MUST BE
DONE IN RED

Policy

from a Principal

The firm will grant, with prior approval, time off with pay for up to a
total of ~~(32)~~ 24 hours to enable employees to take professional licensing
examinations. Employees requiring more than (one attempt) to complete
the examination successfully may take either vacation or time off
without pay.

The firm (does not) pay for preparation courses or
examination fees.

The firm (does) (~~does not~~) pay for initial fee ~~or annual
renewal fee~~ for licensing. *For Project Architects and Project Managers, the firm will pay for annual renewal fees for the State of Colorado.*

6.16 PROFESSIONAL LICENSING AND CERTIFICATION

Policy

The firm will grant, with prior approval from a Principal, time off with
pay for up to a total of 24 hours to enable employees to take
professional licensing examinations. Employees requiring more than one
attempt to complete the examination successfully may take either
vacation or time off without pay.

The firm does not pay for preparation courses or examination fees.

The firm does pay for initial fee for licensing. For Project
Architect's and Project Manager's, the firm will pay for annual renewal
fees for the State of Colorado.

Commentary

In accordance with state law, professional licensing is one condition
for assuming greater professional responsibility. The firm encourages
all eligible employees to obtain their appropriate professional licenses
and/or certifications at the earliest opportunity, regardless of present
assignment.

Automate Hiring

Don't waste your time producing your
employees' resumes. Economize on your
time and their time from the first time
you meet. Have them enter their job and
personal histories into a formated resume
file. This also tests their familiarity
with a keyboard.

During the interview you can review their
resumes on your monitor and make necessary
notes. Rewrite the notes in the same file
and begin building a resume based on the
new information.

This practice also creates a manageable
file of potential talent for your firm.
You are capable of retrieving resumes and
other information for future hiring.
Inadvertently, you will also be able to
judge the computer literacy level of
potential candidates -- unquestionably an
important factor in A/E business.

8 Lower The Overhead

Who forgot to turn off the lights? Who
left all the hot plates on? Who left the
PH meter on? These are the sort of
questions they could have asked at the
Industrial Hygiene Unit at **Galson and
Galson** consulting engineers of East
Syracuse, New York. Instead, in theory at
least, don't ask those questions.

The Industrial Hygiene lab at the
consulting engineering firm has a list
created with a word processor. It is a
simple word processing application that
reduces anxieties -- especially if you are
paying the overhead.

LAST (BUT NOT LEAST) PERSON CHECKLIST FOR THE LAB

IN GENERAL :				
	MONDAY	TUESDAY	WENSDAY	THURSDAY
CHECK SOLVENT STOR. RM.- LIGHT OFF/DOOR SECURE				
DOOR TO STACK LAB. SECURE				
COFFEE POT IN CAFE. TURNED OFF				
TERMINALS OFF-				
ED'S OFFICE				
EVA'S OFFICE				
SIGN IN ROOM				
LAB CORRIDOR				
USER'S ROOM				
HOOD IN LAB OO2-OFF/ CHECK WITH AA PERSON FIRST				
ALL RADIOS OFF				
SAMPLES PUT AWAY				
REAGENTS/SOLVENTS PUT AWAY				
ALL HOODS:				
LIGHTS OFF				
SASH PULLED DOWN				
FANS ON LOW				
VACUUM OFF AND NOT ON CONTINUOUS				
LAB 001 :				
WATER OFF ON ALL CONDENSERS				
ALL HEATING MANTLES OFF				
ALL HOT PLATES OFF				
UV-VIS SPEC. OFF				
LAB 002 :				
CHECK WITH AA OPER. FOR INSTRUMENTS/GASES				
LAB 003 :				
ALL OVENS OFF UNLESS OTHERWISE MARKED				
MUFFLE FURNACE OFF				
AUTOCLAVE OFF				
PH METERS-DISPLAY OFF, ON STAND-BY				
TURDBIDIMETER OFF				
ALL WATER OFF				

Automate Envelopes

Another good word processing practice saves on envelopes. Since you are using a microcomputer to send transmittals and field reports, why not develop a format for a wraparound envelope?

Collaborative Design Group of Tucson, Arizona offers an example. The improvised envelope is nothing more than an attached piece of computer paper. In your format for transmittals and field reports, you set up the previous page for a sender's and recipient's address. In one stroke you generate a correspondence without having to put an envelope in your printer.

(Authors' Note: It is wise to use a heavier paper stock for this idea. Don't wait to find out that the U. S. Postal Service's automatic separators have spliced, sliced up or crumbled your most recent transmittal.)

USP Real Estate Investment Trust
Mary Clemen
4333 Edgewood Road NE
Cedar Rapids, Iowa 52499

COLLABORATIVE DESIGN GROUP 2555 E. FIRST ST. TUCSON ARIZONA 85716

10 Tracking Transmittals

Transmittals forms are used for sending information to clients, contractors, engineering consultants, and government agencies. They serve as reminders of deadlines, construction, and scheduled changes. The forms provide legal proof for A/E's if a contractor fails to perform.

Hundreds of transmittals flow between the numerous parties on a project. The task of keeping a log of the forms often befuddles the most conscientious A/E's.

So before paranoia sets in, keep a log of transmittal forms on your microcomputer with word processing software.

Rex E. Willoughby, AIA, Architect
Blanton & Co. Architects & Engineers
300 W. Paseo Redondo, Tucson 85701

collaborative design group TRANSMITTAL

The Following Items Are Being Tansmitted.
If Not As Indicated Please Notify Sender
At Once

As required by the deed restrictions, we are submitting the attached
    drawings for preliminary approval. The plans are for proposed
    offices for Dr. Robert M. Dryden and Dr. Jorge A. Godinez-Cejudo.
    The City of Tucson, Planning Department has given preliminary
    approval to the site plan as shown. Please feel free to call if
    any questions arise.

We are forwarding the following documents:

        EXTERIOR PERSPECTIVE / COLOR SCHEME
        SITE PLAN / AREA ANALYSIS
        FLOOR PLAN - FIRST FLOOR - DR. DRYDEN
        FLOOR PLAN - SECOND FLOOR - DR. DRYDEN
        ELEVATIONS - DR. DRYDEN
        ELEVATIONS - DR. DRYDEN
        FLOOR PLAN - DR. GODINEZ
        ELEVATIONS - DR. GODINEZ
        ELEVATIONS - DR. GODINEZ
        LANDSCAPE PLAN
        LANDSCAPE LIGHTING PLAN

345 E. TOOLE AVE. SUITE 202 / TUCSON ARIZONA 85701 / (602) 629-9752

11 Tailoring Transmittals

Transmittal forms rank among the worst in design. Few A/E's would argue that the average transmittal form ranks up there with the 1040.

The microcomputer gives A/E's a tool to combat poor form design. It allows you to design your own forms, use your own letterhead so you don't have to repeatedly write that information, and make the project box and date box large enough so no one reads the wrong date.

It allows you to include the categories that are relevant to your work: drawings, specifications, products, meeting minutes, etc. How about giving the remarks column more space? Now, you don't have to cramp your hand penciling in minuscule letters.

12 Killing Alligators

Ever heard the one about "being up to your ears in alligators"? Why be devoured by problems? Organize yourself with a checklist for every project, tasks within a project, client schedule, and government deadlines.

Now you're "up to your ears in a swamp of paper". You have a mechanical, electrical, structural, environmental impact statement checklist, a planning board checklist, a zoning board checklist, and a financial checklist -- to name a few.

Ask your friends for their checklists too. But don't leave them on paper. Put all your checklists into a microcomputer, create printouts for your yourself, and update your computer files regularly -- even have a master checklist for your major checklist items.

TASK DESCRIPTION FOR COMPREHENSIVE CONTRACT DOCUMENT CHECK LIST

Task Number	Task Description	Budget Hours	Hrs to Date	Remarks
A000	Design Development Recap			
3.00	Reaffirm Conformance to:			
001	Architect/Owner Agreements			
002	Architect/Consultant			
003	Approved Program			
004	Production Budget			
005	Construction Budget			
3.000 TO 010		Total		
3.010	Reaffirm Conformance to Regulations			
011	Sponsoring Agency Regulations			
012	Regulatory Agencies			
013	Building Department			
014	Health Department			
015	Public Works Department			
016	Fire Department			
017	Labor Department			
018	Zoning Board			
019	Ainsi			
020	Osha			
021	Other City Agencies			
022	Other State Agencies			
023	Other Federal Agencies			
010 TO 029		Total		
3.030	Verify Internal Document, Coord. & Approvals			
031	Project Checker(s)			
032	Design Department			
033	Production Department			
034	Construction Department			
035	Specification Department			
036	Other Disciplines			
3.030 to 036		Total		

13 Legal Friendships

Prevent a duel at sunrise. Develop a
Fixed Fee Contract so that you and your
consulting A/E have a common understanding
of a project's scope.

Richard A. Ebeltoft, an Arizona structural
engineer, and **Frank Mascia** of the Arizona-
based **Collaborative Design Group** have
formatted a contract with word processing.
Their format includes: date, job number,
job name, definition of contract
agreement, scope of work, etc. Since
their firms work together frequently, the
format stays the same -- and in their
files -- with occasional editing when new
contracts are necessary.

richard a. ebeltoft p.e.
627 e speedway no.1
tucson, arizona 85705
[602] 623—1303

FIXED FEE CONTRACT

Date: March 7, 1986
Job No.   86—12
Job Name: CITRIN RESIDENCE
Architect:CDG Architects
          345 E. Toole
          Tucson, Arizona 85701
          [602] 629—9752

1.0 Contract Agreement

1.1 This agreement made as of the **seventh day of March** in the year of Nineteen
Hundred and Eighty Six.

1.2 Between: **CDG Architects** (hereinafter referred to as the Architect) and:
Richard A. Ebeltoft (hereinafter referred to as the Engineer).

1.3 The Architect and the Engineer agree as set forth below.

This contract is for structural systems engineering services provided to the above
named Architect for the aforementioned project. The terms and conditions of this
contract are listed below.

2.0 Scope of work:

The following list of items covers the approximat. scope of work of this project
taken from your preliminary documents. The extent of the structural engineering
required for each of the items may vary with the review of more complete
documents.

Please review and make any comments or clarifications necessary.

> 2.1 Roof framing design.
> 2.2 Floor framing design.
> 2.3 Wall systems design.
> 2.4 Column systems design.
> 2.5 Foundations design.
> 2.6 Lateral force resisting system design.
> 2.7 Retaining Wall systems design [that are part of building NIC Site retaining
>   walls.
> 2.8 Lateral force resisting system design.

14 Reducing EIS Paperwork

When the Sierra Club, the Wilderness
Society and the Environmental Lobby
persuaded legislators to mandate
environmental impact statements (EIS's),
they were oblivious to the paperwork
armada approaching.

A decade after the EIS has become required
of all local, state, federal, private, and
public projects, A/E's are still
scratching their heads. How can they
streamline EIS production? Once you have
done that one on a microcomputer, you
edit it for all your other EIS's.

(Authors' Note: Do the same with other
planning and zoning documents. Remember,
with word processing software, once you
have a basic document on file, editing
customizes it. Make all the bureaucrats
do the work.)

15 Meeting Minutes Taking

You're taking notes at a design session, client presentation or a job site meeting. Your client has made a new request, one out of whack with what was originally planned.

The contractor scratches his head, dissents, but eventually agrees to the request. You are poised between the two, taking notes with a pencil and paper. Your notes, in fact, substantiate a major change and now take on a legal significance.

Later, at your office, you ask your secretaries to assemble your meeting notes for distribution to all parties -- including your client's lawyers. Your secretaries are dumbfounded because they cannnot read your handwriting.

The solution: Buy a portable computer and format a word processing file before you go to a meeting. Include a format for title, meeting number, time, date, and attendees at the top of the page. At the bottom of the last page, format name, date, issues, and standard notice about acceptance at the meeting. You're not only taking extensive notes, but creating a far more complete record.

When you return to your office, all your secretary has to do is transfer files, edit your typing mistakes, and print out meeting copies. You've now created better records in less time with less effort.

```
OPERATIONS COMMITTEE:  Old South Church, 645 Boylston St, Boston, MA 02116
                       Meeting # 16, Thursday, July 05, 1984, 5:15pm

Present:   Committee;  Rev Crawford; Parkins, Thompson, Wardell, Worth
           Architect;  Coolidge: Shepley, Bulfinch, Richardson, & Abbott
           Other     ;  Clark (part time)
Absent :   Committee;  Brown
```

INSPECTION OF PROJECT Committee members made brief tour to inspect project, understand scope, and see progress.

REVIEW AND APPROVAL OF SUBCONTRACTORS Committe was informed that only one electrical bid was received (from Norton), but that the electrical Company would do the work on a cost plus basis with the bid as an upset. Also that only one Millwork bid was received (from Leeming), but that SBRA asked the contractor to secure an additional bid from Scott & Duncan, giving them more time for estimating. Committe reviewed and approved the following subcontractors :

```
Scaffolding
   Marr Scaffolding     $ 21,690 (12 weeks) Exterior 06-21-1984
   Marr Scaffolding     $132,464 (31 weeks) interior 06-13-1984

Painting
   M.L. McDonald        $103,500                      07-03-1984

Electrical
   Norton Electrical Co. $274,900                     07-03-1984
```

Miscellaneous
As per Walsh Letter 06-13-1984, miscellaneous contractors are approved for negotiating of prices as per Walsh upset figures for the following trades:

```
Masonry                    Pizzotti Bros.
Misc. Metal                American Architectural iron Co.
MTL DRS, Frames, WD Doors  Design Door
Roofing & Copper Work      Gilbert & Becker Co.
Lath & Plaster, GYP WBD    McDonald
Ceramic Tile               Zani Tile Co.
Wood Flooring              M. Frank Higgins Co.
Carpet Installation        M. Frank Higgins Co.
Lift System                Major Theater Equipment Co.
Plumbing, Sprinkler, HVAC  Cleghorn
```

LETTER OF INTENT Tom Wardell furnished original to D. Coolidge for transmittal to Contractor. Contract now being reviewed and prepared by T. Wardell.

DESIGN PRESENTATIONS At the next meeting, SBRA will present finalized design of platform (which includes some patterned parquet flooring), chancel furniture (pulpit modifications, choir benches and chairs, portable font, bishop chair selections and needle-work design suggestions), revised chandelier designs, carpet colors, and pew cushions.

Distribution: 1 Each Committe Member, SBRA, Renovations Committee

07-05-1984   - 1 -   OS_MTG16

16 Drawing Management

Drawing lists are simplified lists of drawings to show your clients how a project develops. They describe drawings needed for schematic developments, furniture layouts, electrical and duct work, reflective ceilings, plumbing, sprinklers, fire alarms, rentals, exterior and interior details, elevators, stairs, food service, and lavatories, among other spaces.

A well-organized drawing list takes on financial significance. It gives A/E's an experience record of how many designs it took to complete a project without dragging out drawings. If the drawing list includes dimensional details, it lends itself to repro budget analysis. It will also tell you about the number of pin-bar layers in a final design, becomes a customized order for reprographics, serves as a basis for a punch list, and becomes a basis for future project planning.

To make your drawing list work for you, keep the list in a word processing file. You can again create your own categories, keep valuable financial information, and make personal notes. When you begin planning your next job, edit the previous drawing list for a similar project.

This example comes from Rolland Thompson's collection:

WEST CONCORD UNION CHURCH
April 29th, 1986
WORKING DRAWING LIST & MAN HOUR PROJECTION

Scale: 1/4 - 1/4" =1'-0"
       1/8 - 1/8" =1'-0"
       3/4 - 3/4" =1'-0"
       1 1/2" - 1 1/2"=1'-0"

Original: M = Mylar, Y = Yellow Trace
  Repro: S = Slick, D = Diazo Reproducible' HS = 1/2 Size
  Prints: B = Blue Line, or Black Line
   Size: 24" x36"; Area: 6.0 sf

Dwg #	Scale	Date	Description	TL	RDT	JG	SP	RDT	RDT	Comments
ARCHITECTURAL										MECHANICAL
Cover	o	08/31	Exterior Perspect.		4					Revise existing perspective
Plans										M301 Details
L001	1"=20'	"	INFO + SITE	4	4	40			4	L100U Site Utilities
A200	*1/4"	"	LOWER LEVEL	4	8	80			8	M200 Lower Level
A201	* "	"	SANCTUARY	8	8			80	8	M201 Sanctuary Level
A203	* "	"	2nd FLOOR			20			4	M202 2nd Floor
Reflected Ceiling										ELECTRICAL - POWER
A200R	*1/4"	"	LOWER LEVEL CLG				4		4	E200P Lower Level
A201R	* "	"	SANCTUARY CLG				4		4	E201P Sanctuary Level
										E202P 2nd Floor/Details
Elevations + Sections										
A301	1/4"	"	NORTH		4		6	2	2	ELECTRICAL - LIGHTING
A302	"	"	EAST				6	2	2	E200 Lower Level
A303	"	"	SOUTH				6	2	2	E201 Sanctuary Level
A304	"	"	WEST				6	2	2	E202 2nd Floor/Details
A306	"	"	S-N ——>W		4		16		4	ELCTRICAL - MISC
A307	"	"	N-S ——>E		4		16		4	E301 Details, Schedules
A308	"	"	E-W ——>S		4		16		4	PLUMBING
Details										P201 Sprinklers
A401	AN	"	PINE STREET ENTR	2	4			60	4	P301 Details
A402	"	"	NARTHEX, SANCTUARY	8	8	52	8		4	Floor plans are developed as measured
A403	"	"	SANCTUARY, ELEVATO	4	4	52	8		4	drawings on CAD. Clone and convert to
A404	"	"	GLASS, STORM SASH, \ETC			52	8		4	design drawings for completion of DD,
A405	"	"	BATHROOMS, CLOSETS	DRS		52	8		4	then develop as working dwgs. Electri-
A406	"	"	CLOSETS, MILLWORK			52	8		4	cal drawings will be converted to post
A407	"	"	(SPARE)			52	8		4	punched overlay drafting. Same for
Interior Perspective				8	16					Sprinkler set.
Schedules			FINISH/DOOR/WINDOW	2	4			8	8	
Specifications			(info giving, etc)		4				12	
Meeting/ Reports									60	
Bidding/Receipt									24	
					(80)			(204)	(168)	= 468 (RDT only)
				40	80	532		204	168	= 1030 = 60% man years

17 Overseeing Drawings

Managing working drawings is nothing short
of a nightmare -- unless you are a
fastidious person. Every iteration,
alteration, preliminary approval and final
approval demands extensive documentation.
Sloppy notes on scattered sheets on your
desk promise to delay projects -- not to
mention the confidence of your client and
contractor.

Turn your microcomputer into an overseer
of your working drawings. This is easily
accomplished with modification of your
drawing list. Delete unnecessary
categories and add ones for working
drawings (such as 60%, 90%, Coordinated,
100%, Bid, Addenda #, Change #, Date). Now
you have a customized file that tells the
status of all your design efforts.

18 Customize Repro Form

Here's a follow-up idea that transforms
the overlay drawing list into a repro
order form. Why fill out a reprographic
house's order form? They usually ask for
the same information you already have on
one of your other lists.

Take the overlay drawing list, reformat it
to reflect the reprographic house's form,
and you're in business.

In fact, you can endear yourself to the
reprographic house by including necessary
(though overlooked) information about
screening and other enhancements. All in
all, your microcomputer personalizes and
fully defines what used to be a major
paperwork hassle.

Louis DiPaolo of **GSO Graphics, Inc.** in New
York City and Rolland Thompson produced
this example:

TODD LEE/F R CLARK Associates, Inc.
148 State Street
Boston, MA 02109   * = Screened

Project Name: SIDEWALK NO. 1
Project Nos.: 8627, 8627.A thru G
Date: June 23, 1986   *6/24/86*

OVERLAY PLAN: * = screened; ** = furniture, signage, rental plans, security, etc.

DRAWING # DESCRIPTION · OVERLAYS · REPRO ORDER FORM
Drawing Size: 24" x 36" — 6.0 SF

DRAWING #	DESCRIPTION	I arch w. grid	II arch no grid	III arch notes	IV consult drawing	V ** arch. overlay	Slick	Blue Line	Ozal -id	Mylar	8 1/2x11
SITEWORK											
L-200	Contours		survey		1-200	L-200					
L-201	Paving		survey		1-201	L-201					
L-202	Planting		survey		1-202	L-202					
CIVIL											
C-200	Civil, Grades										
C-201	Utilities										
C-202	Site Lighting										
STRUCTURAL											
S-200	Foundation	a-200g *			S-200			③↓			
S-201	1st Floor	a-201g *			S-201						
S-202	2nd Floor	a-202g *			S-202						
S-203/6	3rd-6th Floors	a-203g *			S-203/6						
S-207	Roof	a-207g *			S-207						
ARCHITECTURAL											
A-200	Basement	a-200g		A-200			③↓	⑤↓			
A-201	1st Floor	a-201g		A-201							
A-202	2nd Floor	a-202g		A-202							
A-203/6	3rd-6th Floor	a-203/6g		A-203/6							
A-207	Roof	a-207g		A-207							
A-208	Lobby/Toilets	a-208g		A-208							
REFLECTED CLG											
A-201R	RF 1st Floor		a-201	A-201R			③↓	⑤↓			
A-202R	RF 2nd Floor		a-202	A-202R							
A-203/6R	RF 3rd-6th Fl		a-203/6	A-203/6							
ELEVATIONS											
A-301	N/S Elevations		a-301	A-301				②↓	①↓		
A-302	E/W Elevations		a-302	A-302							
A-303	AA/BB Sections		a-303	A-303							
MECHANICAL											
M-200	Basement	a-200g *			M-200						
M-201	1st Floor	a-201g *			M-201						
M-202	2nd Floor	a-202g *			M-202						
M-203/6	3rd-6th Floors	a-203/6g *			M-203/6						
M-207	Roof	a-207g *			M-207						
ELECTRICAL-P											
E-200P	Basement	a-200g *			E-200P						
E-201P	1st Floor	a-201g *			E-201P						
E-202P	2nd Floor	a-202g *			E-203P						
E-203P	3rd-6th Floors	a-203/6g *			E-203/6P						
E-207P	Roof	a-207g *			E-207P						
ELECTRICAL-L											
E-200L	Basement	a-200g *			E-200L						
E-201L	1st Floor	a-201g *			E-201L						
E-202L	2nd Floor	a-202g *			E-202L						
E-203L	3rd-6th Floors	a-203/6g *			E-203/6L						
E-307L	Roof	a-207g *			E-207L						
PLUMBING											
P-200	Basement	a-200g *			P-200						
P-201	1st Floor	a-201g *			P-201						
	CONTINUED										

Todd Lee/F R Clark Associates, Inc.   - 1 -   SIDEWALK.DWG

19 Spotlight on Lighting

It's amazing how many graphic schedules end up on a drawing. It's also amazing to think that they have such symbolic significance. Lighting schedules show each fixture type, manufacturer's catalogue numbers, finish, lamps, wattage and associated details. A/E's are understandably concerned about keeping track of current specifications. One mistake, and the client could end up with an incandescent lamp, rather than a fluorescent tube, or incomplete compatible color and finishes.

Keep track of your schedules -- lighting, door, window, cabinets, etc. Such a list will have enduring value throughout a project. Its electrical users will include electrical engineers, lighting designers, electrical contractors, and the supply houses. With customized projects, the schedules reinforce the specifications for manufacturer bidding.

Berg/Howland Associates, architects and lighting designers in Boston, Massachusetts created this example:

Berg/Howland Associates
Architects & Lighting Designers

Lighting Fixture Schedule

Type	Diagram	Manufacturer	Lamp	Notes
IG-1		Kim 4000N accent light	30R20 or 50R20	Optional spear or tree mount
Alt.		Kim ELN-21 accent light		Optional spear mount
IG-2		Kim 4005N accent light	75 or 150w PAR38/SP or FL	Optional spear or tree mount
IG-3		Kim 4010N accent light	75 or 150w PAR38 or R40, SP or FL	Optional tree mount
IG-4		Kim 5150 well light	75 or 150w PAR38/SP or FL	
IG-5		Sterner OFL-36/BZ/PAR36/12/ D/C/WS fountain light	36PAR36Q/ WFL	
IG-6		Custom bollard light		Deleted

20 Bidding Relief

Aren't A/E's supposed to be designers and not bureaucrats? Keep all your bid records in your word processing files, including bidding instruction sheets, description of the bids, legal issues, location of drawings, and bid bonds.

Like other word processing applications, this one reduces the amount of paperwork the second and third times around -- not the first. You still update information specific for each project but not general text. When you do, you are in great shape to crank out bidding information endlessly.

Rolland Thompson provides this example:

INFORMATION FOR BIDDERS

Owner: (Fill in name of Owner) **

Project: (Fill in location and name of project)

1. Receipt of Bids

   The Owner may consider informal and bid not prepared and submitted in
   accordance with the provisions of the Bidding and Contract Documents
   and may waive any informalities in or reject any or all bids and is
   under no obligation to accept the lowest bidder. Any bid may be
   withdrawn to the scheduled time for the receipt of bids or authorized
   postponement thereof and any bid received after such time and within
   sixty (60) days after the actual date of the opening thereof. Bids
   shall not contain and recapitulation of the Work to be done. No oral,
   telegraphic or telephonic bids or modifications shall be considered.

2. Definitions

   Bidding and Contract Documents are those items enumerated in the Table
   of Contents attached herein before and all addenda, change orders and
   any supplementary data together with all provisions of law deemed to be
   inserted.

3. Preparation of Bids

A. Bids must be submitted on the prescribed forms. All blank spaces and
   applicable description of work to be furnished as listed hereinafter
   must be typed or printed in. All blank spaces for alternates as
   applicable to the contract work to be furnished and outlned in Division
   1, Section 1B as hereinafter described must be filled in using both
   words and figures. Conditional bids shall not be accepted.

B. Bids that are illegible or that contain omissions, alternatives,
   additions or items not called for in the Bidding and Contract Documents
   as listed hereinafter may be rejected as informal. In the event any
   bidder modifies, limits or retricts all or any part of such a bid in a
   manner other than that expressly provided for in the bidding documents,
   such bid may be rejected as informal.

C. Additional copies of Form of Bid and Form of Bid Bond are available
   free of charge upon request from (Fill in name of Owner or Architect,
   whichever applies).

4. Examination of Bidding and Contract Documents

A. Prospective bidders shall examine the Bidding and Contract Documents as
   listed hereinafter and carefully, and before bidding, shall make
   written request to the owner for an interpretation or correction if any
   ambiguity, inconsistency, or error therein which should be discovered
   by a reasonably prudent bidder. Every request for such interpretation
   must be received at least five days prior to the date fixed for the
   receipt of bids. Such interpretation or correction as well as any

   (** Check all underlined portions for completion or revision)

Rolland D. Thompson   2.09   Construction Administration

21 The Science of Advertising

Don't become a "Madison Avenue" advertising agency. When you must advertise for bidding contractors, don't write your own ads. Why should you?

You probably learned about the project from an advertisement. Enter that advertisement into a word processing file. Then, whenever you send a project out to bid, customize it for your demands, and send off a printout to **The Commerce Business Daily** or whatever publication is appropriate.

<u>INVITATION TO BIDDERS</u>

1. **INVITATION:** You are invited to submit a stipulated sum bid for the Construction Work, including Plumbing, Heating, Ventilating, Air Conditioning; Electrical and Site Development Work for the proposed new construction identified as: <u>(Revise scope as required)</u> **

<u>Location and Official Name of Project</u>

2. **DATE:** Sealed proposals for all the Work will be received at the office of the <u>Owner (or the Architect)</u>

    <u>Name of Owner (or Architect)</u>
    <u>Street Address</u>
    <u>City, State, Zip</u>

    on or before <u>2:00 PM E.D.T</u> (or other Time), <u>Day of Week, Date, Month, Year.</u> <u>Bids will be opened privately at a later date.</u> (or <u>Bids will be opened at time and date listed above</u>). Envelopes containing proposals must be clearly marked with the name of the Project, and be addressed to:

    Representative of Owner (or Architect)

    at the above address.

3. **BIDDING AND CONTRACT DOCUMENTS:** A complete set of Bidding and Contract Documents are provided to the Invited Bidders at no charge. Additional sets must be purchased on a <u>non-</u>refund basis, at <u>$ .00</u> per set which includes mailing charges. <u>(or whatever different arrangement the owner or agency requires).</u>

4. **WITHDRAWAL OF BID:** No Bidder may withdraw his bid within <u>60</u> days after the actual date of bid opening.

                        By:_____
                           <u>(Project Architect)</u>
                           <u>(Name of Architectural Firm)</u>

                        For: <u>(Name of Owner)</u>

Rolland D. Thompson   2.09   Construction Administration

22 Abbreviate Like A Pro

Don't put your creative energy into
abbreviations for drawings. It's a time-
consuming and dangerous practice. Bad
abbreviations -- especially personal ones
that make little sense -- will help a
lawyer tie a noose around your neck.

"Isn't Al, the recognized abbreviation for
aluminum?" the lawyer asked. "Yes, but I
thought it boring, so I used A for
aluminum, and AL for Alley Lighting."

Make masterlists of abbreviations in a
word processing file. Enter your own
in-house list, lists from organizations
and associations, fellow professionals and
graphic standards books. Set up an
alphabetized masterlist of abbreviations
and definitions, and then set up another
alphabetized list of definitions with
corresponding abbreviations. The first
list becomes the drawing information
sheet. The second printout goes to the
drafter.

Irving Levett of Richmond, Virginia
devised the abbreviations in the
accompanying example:

ABBREVIATIONS FOR CONTRACT DRAWINGS

AB	above	BLK	block(work)
AFF	above finished floor	BLKG	blocking
ACC	access	BD	board
ACCY	accessory	BS	both sides
ACD	access door	BW	both ways
ACFL	access floor	BOT	bottom
AP	access panel	BCB	bottom of curb
AC	acoustical	BOF	bottom of footing
ACP	acoustical panel	BOP	bottom of pit
ACT	acoustical tile	BOW	bottom of wall
ACPL	acoustical plaster	BKT	bracket
ACR	acrylic plastic	BRK	brick(work)
ADD	addendum	BRG	bridge
ADH	adhesive	BCL	broom closet
ADJ	adjacent	BRZ	bronze
ADJT	adjustable	BLDG	building
AGG	aggregate	BUR	built up roofing
AC	air conditioner	BBD	bulletin board
ALT	alternative		
AL	aluminum	CAB	cabinet
ANC	anchor, anchorage	CAD	cadmium
AB	anchor bolt	CPT	carpet(ed)
ANOD	anodized	CSMT	casement
APPR	approved	CI	cast iron
APX	approximate	CIP	cast-in-place
ARCH	architect(ural)	CIPC	cast-in-place concrete
AD	area drain	CST	cast stone
ASB	asbestos	CB	catch basin
ASPH	asphalt	CK	caulk(ing), calk(ing)
AT	asphalt tile	CLG	ceiling
ASSM	assembly	CHT	ceiling height
AUTO	automatic	CEM	cement
		CPL	cement plaster
BP	base plate	CTR	center
BJ	bar joist	CM	centimeter(s)
BALC	balcony	CER	ceramic
BSMT	basement	CT	ceramic tile
B	bathroom	CMT	ceramic mosaic tile
BM	beam	CHBD	chalkboard
BRG	bearing	CHAM	chamfer
BPL	bearing plate	CR	chromium (plated)
BJT	bed joint	CIR	circle
BR	bedroom	CIRC	circumference
BMK	bench mark	CLER	clear(ance)
BEL	below	CLK	clock
BET	between	CL	closet
BVL	beveled	CLS	closure
BIT	bituminous	CCL	clothes closet

23 Personalize Change Proposals

Another form demanding a major overhaul is the change proposal used during construction. Edit an existing change proposal on your microcomputer. Keep the form in your memory for alterations on a job-by-job basis.

You should include headings for the contractor: Cost Calculations, Construction Schedule, Revised Construction Schedule, List of Previous Change Proposal Documents. Also, you shouldn't forget yourselves. Make space for Proposal Change Numbers and the Owner's Change Number.

Once you're comfortable with the new form, you don't have to change its format during a job. Use the same form, just update it, print it out and send it to the general contractor, owner, and whomever else requires notice. The microcomputer serves as a historian for the job -- and a witness if your contractor goofs and points a finger at you.

24 Shine at The Kickoff

Ever have the feeling that you blew it during an on-site kickoff meeting? You failed to persuade everyone of your competence and command of the project. After reading your package of schedules and specifications, the contractors cleared their throats and raised their eyebrows more than once.

Did you not hand out well organized and explicit information? Perhaps not. It wouldn't be the first time that an A/E faced the wrath of project planning. In the future, impress everyone at the kickoff meeting with a brilliant presentation. And do it repeatedly using the same principles stated throughout this book. Do your specification and schedules right the first time, and you have a strong model for repeated presentation.

Rolland Thompson created this example:

Construction Administration

<u>CONSIDERATIONS FOR CONSTRUCTION ORIENTATION MEETING</u>

1. INTRODUCTION
   Introduce Project * Special Design Goals
   Introduce Personnel involved * Owner, Architect, Consultants,
       Contractactor, Subcontractors, User (if not owner), etc.
   Distribute Directory

2. HOUSEKEEPING
   Status of Performance Bond, and Labor & Material Payment Bond A311
   Contractor to file certififcate of Insurance (G705).
   Contractors List of Subcontractors.
       Procedures of rejections & substitutions.
   Schedule of Shop Drawings.
   Estimated Progress Schedule and/or CPM.
   Contractors requirements for copies of Contract Documents.
   Project Directory (See introduction above).
   Owners Applications for permanent utilities.
   Owner to file property Insurance with GC.
       Or if Contractor, initiate Change Order.
       Ditto Special Hazards Insurance

3. SCHEDULE OF JOB MEETINGS

4. SHOP DRAWING SUBMITTALS
   CSI designation
   No. of Sepia(s) and Print(s)
   Normal Distribution
   Special Distribution
   Method of Delivery (mail, messenger, etc.)
   On-site-Representatives Involvement

5. SUBSTITUTIONS
   Written Notice
   Documentation of characteristics
   Owner's Benefit = Credit, faster delivery, availability, better
       quality, etc.

6. SAMPLES
   Number of regular samples (review)
   On-site-samples
   Shop mock-up samples

7. PROCEDURES FOR PAYMENT
   Monthly review at job meeting of draft, including comparison with
       previous month and on site inspection (off site inspection if
       applicable).
   Agreement with schedule of Values
   Form of back-up, especially for authorized changes not yet   priced.

8. PROCEDURES FOR CHANGE ORDERS
   Initiation of Change Orders
   Request for Proposals
   Change Orders
       Field Orders
       Authorizations to Proceed
   Claims, disputes, etc.

25 Create Punch List

The punch list accounts for each aspect of construction. It is used to zero in on improper, incomplete, and missing work. A list can include hundreds or even thousands of items. Like a drawing list and schedules, the punch list is another piece of paperwork perfect for a microcomputer application.

At your office, input all of the list's items into a file -- and then have your on-site representative keep track of the items on a microcomputer. Daily maintenance of the punch list and frequent distribution of printouts will simplify completion of a project. It also will reduce the tension that often occurs during final inspection.

MEMORANDUM

5 December, 1983

TO: [General Contractor]

FM: Todd Lee/FR Clark Associates, Inc.

RE: SUBSTANTIAL COMPLETION PUNCH LIST # 12-03-1983
        Project No: 8201

Following is list of outstanding punch list items as of December 03,
1983 related to substantial completion of Renovations, Construction
Contract # 2.

01700 CONTRACT CLOSEOUT
       .01 Clean waterproofing compound from column at NW corner of
            planter # 1.

02550 ADJUSTING TOPS OF UTILITY STRUCTURES TO GRADE
       .02 Adjust utility covers along granite curbing on island
            between canopy and existing parking sign to allow proper
            setting of interlocking pavers.

02612 BRICK PAVERS
       .03 Replace several cracked bricks under canopy, south side
            close to entrance.
       .04 Fill-in with well tamped brick dust at manhole, west of
            paving at north parking area (in lieu of resetting manhole
            height and surrounding with precisely cut concrete pavers).

02613 CONCRETE INTERLOCKING PAVERS
       .05 Replace broken pavers in field of pavers
       .06 Replace poorly set pavers along granite curbing
       .07 Fill-in occasional missing paver pieces along granite
            curbing, in northwest & southwest corners of south parking
            area, around small utility cover between canopy and planted
            area.

01720 PROJECT RECORD DOCUMENTS
       .08 Submit project record drawings and specifications.

01750 WARRANTIES AND BONDS
       .09 07120: Fluid Applied Waterproofing
       .10 07175: Water Repellant Coating
       .11 07240: Exterior Insulated Wall Systems
       .12 07253: Sprayed Fireproofing
       .13 07550: Inverted Roofing
       .14 07600: Flashing and Sheet Metal
       .15 07800: Roof Accessories
       .16 07920: Sealants & Calking
       .17 08410: Aluminum Entrance, Window Wall & Vault
       .18 08450: Revolving Door

26 The Dispatch

When you visit a project, you are there to take notice. Is the roofing under way? Is the A/C equipment lifted into place? Did your message about nailing make it through a chain of command? Is the driveway done?

The questions abound, and they grow in number with each succeeding visit. How do you keep track of the growing number of concerns and complaints? Take copious notes in the field, by hand, or better yet, with a portable computer -- and develop a highly readable format in a word processing file for a field report. Make sure it is easy to fill in, too. Then, when you need to spill your brains on a visit, you just do it.

Collaborative Design Group of Tucson, Arizona writes all its field reports on a microcomputer. The form includes a space for the client's name, project name, number, date, time of visit, specific items, general notes, and a place for its own address.

USP Real Estate Investment Trust
Mary Clemen   PROJECT: Midway Business
4333 Edgewood Road NE
Cedar Rapids, Iowa 52499   PROJECT NUMBER: 8527

FIELD REPORT

The Following Items Were Noted.

Oct 22, 1985
9:30 AM

Reroofing work under way:
Suite 55: Rosin sheet and base sheet nailed; and 15# sheet mopped and
          in place.
          Wall flashing rosin and base sheets being nailed; noted to
          lead man that wall flashing seemed too loose.
Suite 54: Rosin sheet and base sheet being nailed.

General Notes: A/C equipment being lifted in place above roof and
          roofed below. Approved this process. There is no real
          difference from specification.

          Questioned Wayne Vose about nailing of wall flashing rather
          than mopping as per specifications. We will meet to review
          the wall flashing details.

          The apparent areas of heavy debris embedment noted on roof
          above suite 55 were in fact not debris. The irregularities
          were deposits of residue from an asphalt glazing on the
          original roof. These deposits will be eliminated in the
          reroofing process.

27 Do Unlike The Egyptians

Architectural historians would have had an easier job today if Egyptian A/E's had kept a master list of warehoused drawings of the pyramids and other great public works of the pharoahs.

Thirty centuries from now historians will have a different set of worries. They will not have to look hard for the drawings of our great public works -- or for your warehoused drawings. No, instead they will whirl floppies or futuristic equivalents into their computers (if they call them that) and locate your drawings at the Library of Congress.

Begin helping these historians -- and yourselves -- by keeping warehouse information. Base it on your drawing lists, with new categories such as location, storage method, and drawing number. In the short term, you will have no reason to play historian yourself.

The **Old South Church** of Boston, Massachusetts supplied the example:

INVENTORY OF OLD SOUTH DRAWINGS

TYPE	DRAWING #	DATE	REVISION	SCALE	DESCRIPTION	BP	BL	STOR	OZA	VEL	MYL	STOR	NG

** ALLEN & COLLENS

TYPE	DRAWING #	DATE	REVISION	SCALE	DESCRIPTION	BP	BL	STOR	OZA	VEL	MYL	STOR	NG
arch	1	08-10-31	09-21-31	1/4	Basement Floor Plan	1		roll					
"	2	"	"	"	First Floor Plan	"		"					
"	3	"	"	"	Mezzanine Floor Plan	"		"					
"	4	"	"	"	Second Floor Plan	"		"					
"	5	"	"	"	Third Floor Plan	"		"					
"	6	"	"	"	Fourth Floor Plan	"		"					
"	7	"	"	"	Roof Plan	"		"					
"	8	"	"	"	East and South Elevations	"		"					
"	9	"	"	"	North Elevations	"		"					
"	10	"	"	"	West Elevation	"		"					
"	11	"	"	"	Transverse Section	"		"					
"	12	"	"	"	Longitudinal Section	"		"					
"	13	"	"	"	Sections CC, DD	"		"					
"	14	"	"	"	South Elevations, Tower	"		"					

** SHEPLEY BULFINCH RICHARDSON AND ABBOTT, INC.

TYPE	DRAWING #	DATE	REVISION	SCALE	DESCRIPTION	BP	BL	STOR	OZA	VEL	MYL	STOR	NG
arch	Cover	04-23-84	06-08-84	1/4	cover sheet	2		roll	1			flat	1
"	A-1	"	"	"	Basement Plan	"	"	"		"		"	"
"	A-2	"	"	"	Main Floor Plan	"	"	"		"		"	"
"	A-3	"	"	"	Balcony Level Plan	"	"	"		"		"	"
"	A-4	"	"	"	Reflected Ceiling Plans	"	"	"		"		"	"
"	A-5	"	"	"	Section Looking North	"	"	"		"		"	"
"	A-6	"	"	"	Section Looking East	"	"	"		"		"	"
"	A-7	"	"	"	Section Looking South	"	"	"		"		"	"
"	A-8	"	"	"	Section Looking West	"	"	"		"		"	"
"	A-9	"	"	AN	Chancel Platform Details	"	"	"		"		"	"
"	A-10	"	"	AN"	Finish Schedule, Roof Plan, Lantern Detail	"	"	"		"		"	"
"	A-11	"	"	AN"	Woodwork Details	"	"	"		"		"	"
"	A-12				(Not included)								
"	A-13	"	"	AN	HC Toilet, Vestibule Elevs. & Details	"	"	"		"		"	"
demo	D-1	"	"	"	Main Floor Plan	"	"	"		"		"	"
"	D-2	"	"	"	Balcony Level Plan	"	"	"		"		"	"
"	D-3	"	"	"	Longitudinal Section	"	"	"		"		"	"
stru	S-1	"	"	1/8,1/2	Plan & Sections	"	"	"		"		"	"
"	S-2	"	"	1/2,1/4	Sections & Details	"	"	"		"		"	"
mech	M-1	"	"	1/4	HVAC/Plumbing Basement Floor Plan	"	"	"		"		"	"
"	M-2	"	"	"	HVAC/Plumbing Main Floor Plan	"	"	"		"		"	"
"	M-3	"	"	AN	Details	"	"	"				"	
elec	E-1	"	"	1/4	Basement Electrical Layout	"	"	"		"		"	"
"	E-2	"	"	1/4	Basement Electrical Layout	"	"	"		"		"	"
"	E-3	"	"	"	Power & Signal Layout	"	"	"		"		"	"
"	E-4	"	"	"	Balcony Level Electrical Plan	"	"	"		"		"	"
"	E-5	"	"	"	Sanctuary Lighting Plan	"	"	"		"		"	"
"	E-6	"	"	AN	Electrical Riser Diagram	"	"	"		"		"	"

** CASSAVANT FRERES, Saint Hyacinthe, Quebec

TYPE	DRAWING #	DATE	REVISION	SCALE	DESCRIPTION	BP	BL	STOR	OZA	VEL	MYL	STOR	NG
Orgn	D-83-35-H	02-04-84		1/4	West Gallery Organ -Plan/Elevations	"		File					
"	D-83-35-H1	"		1/2,3/4	West Gallery Organ - Details	"		"					
orgn	D-83-35-H2	"		1/4	West Gallery Organ - Elev./Anchor Bolts	"		"					

Storage: BP=Blue Print/BLL= Blue or Black Line/OZA=Ozalid reproducible/VEL=Vellum/MYL=Mylar/NG=8 1/2"x11" photo neg
Stor: Roll= Rolled drawing or Tube/flat=flat dwg file/file=filing cabinet/all 8 /12"x11" negatives are in vault.

28 Help At Project Completion

End a construction contract with global
commands on your word processing software?
As the average A/E knows, the end of a
contract is the time to check all
references in guarantees, warranties and
operating instructions. Unfortunately, if
this means re-reading every piece of paper
generated for the project, it's very time-
consuming.

Here's where the global command takes on
importance. Select pertinent words and
phrases and ask your microcomputer to do
the work. It loves to sort, file, index
and beep through its data. Remember
electrons move faster than the eye.

Spreadsheet

SPREAD SHEET - HEAT LOSS - BUILDING A

ROOM	DOORS	WINDOWS	WALL
LIVING ROOM			
KITCHEN			
CLOSET A			
BEDROOM			
BEDROOM B			
BEDROOM C			
FAMILY R			
BATHR			
CLOSET			

Imagine that you had a calculator in your mind. Whenever you wanted to know how much money you spent on groceries one month, you could read the weekly grocery list, totaling as you go.

Unfortunately, the human mind does not have the calculating or memory abilities to accomplish this task. That is one of the reasons why microcomputer electronic spreadsheets have become so popular. They are relatively inexpensive tools that remember the number of apples and their prices -- and tally the results automatically.

Spreadsheet software is set up like accounting worksheets. On your microcomputer screen you will see the worksheet is divided into columns and rows. Each intersection is called a cell. The location of each cell is indicated just as you would name an intersection on a street map: by naming the two streets that cross to form that intersection.

On the worksheet, the north-south streets are called "columns" or "fields" and are labeled with letters. For example, A is the grocery list for week one. The east-west streets are called "rows", "lines", or "records" and are labeled with numbers. 1 is the apple category. So the cell address A1 signifies the quantity of apples bought during week one.

Into the cells you can put various and sundry kinds of information: numbers or text. A third possibility is a mathematical formula (sometimes of great complexity) that will allow you not just to add and subtract but also to do sophisticated mathematical or statistical analysis.

29 Make 007 Proud

Discovering new leads is an unending process. No A/E firm has a secret. It comes from good detective work from your staff members. Whenever they go into the field, or talk to current clients, they should cleverly ask about possible work.

And, when the leads begin flowing in torrents, there should be a systematic collection, sifting and follow-up process. **The Troyer Group** in Mishawaka, Indiana uses a spreadsheet to tabulate all the leads from firm staff on a weekly basis. This spreadsheet is compiled by the marketing department and distributed to persons in charge. Such a practice serves to tip people off to new ideas, old relationships, etc.

The spreadsheet is based on an information sheet developed by the firm. It includes sections for lead status (new, potential, update), date, project titles, contact name and address, appropriate firm division, potential fees, starting dates, probability rating on a scale of 0-10 (0=dead, 10=signed contract). The information sheet also has a section for market segment.

```
THE TROYER GROUP
Weekly Lead Report                       New Leads Received:   May 5-9, 1986              [SAMPLE]

                                                                  Est.              Est.
CD No.     Title/Description              Contact        Service  Fees    Rating    Start    PIC
=================================================================================================

6101.00    Second Presbyterian Church    Roger Jones    A/E      18,000   5        8/86     ABR
              Planning large addition to present
              facility.  Uptown, WI.

6102.00    Jameson University Conference Center  Charles Bobbyck  A/E  58,000  2    1/87     TRL
              Received tip that Jameson may be
              considering new conference center
              adjoining fine arts building.
              Merideth, KS.

6103.00    Conway Center Schools--Energy  Tony Rondo     A/E      22,000   8        7/86     SYS
              From·published notice seeking A/E
              services for a variety of energy-
              related projects throughout
              district.  Conway Center, IN.

6044.00    Casa Loma Department Stores    Randall Friesen  CPM    85,000   4        5/87     LTE
              Opportunity to provide CPM services
              for new warehouse and office project.
              Sidra, OK.

6166.00    Divine Mercy Hospital          Fr. Frances Lynd  A/E   250,000  2        9/86·    TRL
              Board considering moving ahead with
              new wing and retirement community
              development.  Interview is being sched-
              uled for next month.  Petersborough, IN.
                                                        ------------
                                          Weighted fees:  122,200
```

30 Weighing Clues

The Troyer Group of Mishawaka, Indiana summarizes all the leads, and issues reports regularly.

The reports are edited forms of the same spreadsheet in previous example except that they are broken down by staff members name, dollar value per lead and ratings. Leads resulting in either signed contracts or dead ends are eliminated from the system.

```
LEADS FOLLOW UP BY:                  REPORT DATE:
      Larry D. Roland, AIA              01-May-86
                                                  RATING:
RESP SER        PROJECT TITLE          CONTACT    INIT CURR SPEC.SERV.   FEE    EMPL  INITIAL    START    FOLLOW UP
LDR  475 Lincoln Insurance Center      Keith Holloway    9   9  COMM PS  $1,500 SRT  25-Apr-86  01-Jul-86 10-Jun-86
LDR   89 Main Street Presbyterian Church  Rev. Bob Monroe 9   9  CHUR A  $25,000 LDR 18-Mar-85  01-Jun-86 01-Aug-86
LDR  125 Manitok Baptist Church        Freeman Lesch     2   9  CHUR A  $26,000 SRT  18-Apr-85  15-May-86 05-May-86
LDR  476 Lincoln Insurance Center      Keith Holloway    8   8  COMM A  $28,000 SRT  25-Apr-86  01-Jul-86 10-Jun-86
LDR  169 Second Mennonite Church, Antioch Ralph Zehr     8   8  CHUR A  $35,000 LDR  30-May-85  01-Apr-86 01-Aug-86
LDR  155 Northern Baptist Chapel       Roger Harnish     4   5  CHUR A  $35,000 TDF  01-May-85  10-Sep-86 01-Oct-86
LDR  332 St. Francis Catholic Church   ?                 3   5  CHUR A  $30,000 LDR  22-Oct-85  01-Jun-86 01-May-86
LDR  171 Newton Church of the Savior   Sam Menkamp       5   4  CHUR A  $25,000 LDR  30-May-85  10-Sep-86 05-May-86
LDR  273 Christian Church of Parrish   Rev. Carol Dunn   6   1  CHUR A  $60,000 LDR  25-Sep-85  01-Jun-86 01-May-86
LDR  387 Manor Presbyterian Retreat Center Bill Noble    1   1  CHUR PS  $2,000 RWD  03-Dec-85  15-Mar-86 05-May-86
LDR  264 Maven Office Center           John Peters       7   1  COMM A  $85,000 TSP  13-Sep-85  01-May-86 05-May-86
LDR  446 Mission Valley Rest Home      Sanford Lear      1   1  RET  PS  $5,000 LDR  28-Feb-86  01-Apr-86 05-May-86
LDR  448 Mission Valley Rest Home      Sanford Lear      1   1  RET  S   $5,000 LDR  28-Feb-86  01-Apr-86 05-May-86
LDR  447 Mission Valley Rest Home      Sanford Lear      1   1  RET  A  $55,000 LDR  28-Feb-86  01-Apr-86 05-May-86
LDR  313 Savoy Nursing Home            Lon Terry         6   1  RET  A  $75,000 KJM  02-Oct-85  01-Aug-86 01-Jul-86
LDR  397 Simtech Energy Center         Richard Black     2   1  COMM A  $20,000 LDR  11-Dec-85  01-Jun-86 01-May-86
```

```
          SUMMARY:                       DOLLARS    RATED $'s
          =======================================  ===========
          Leads of = RATING "0"............!       $0         $0
          Leads of = RATING "1"............! $307,000     $30,700
          Leads of = RATING "2"............!       $0         $0
          Leads of = RATING "3"............!       $0         $0
          Leads of = RATING "4"............!  $25,000     $10,000
          Leads of = RATING "5"............!  $65,000     $32,500
          Leads of = RATING "6"............!       $0         $0
          Leads of = RATING "7"............!       $0         $0
          Leads of = RATING "8"............!  $63,000     $50,400.
          Leads of = RATING "9"............!  $52,500     $47,250
          Leads of = RATING "10"...........!       $0         $0
                                            ===========  ===========
                           TOTALS........! $512,500    $170,850
```

31 The Big Pieces

The Troyer Group then breaks down the spreadsheet into the four profit centers of the firm.   This tells the firm where each profit center stands.   At The Troyer Group, the profit centers include planning services, construction project management, architecture, engineering, and site/civil.

For each of the centers, the marketing department also generates an overall dollar value of potential leads and the firm's cut of the pie.

32 A Cash Stream

Avoid trouble at your bank. Use a spreadsheet to set up a cash flow account. This account will induce you to keep your invoices timely. It will force you to face your creditors. You also can keep your consulting engineers happy with scheduled payments.

Thus, you are raising your stock in the contractor's mind, while holding your client accountable. Many architects end up doing the engineer's on-site work because of a failure to pay them in a timely fashion.

33 Weighing Options

When you consider a major equipment purchase, you should depend on your spreadsheet. Its ability to list alternatives and data about alternatives simplifies weighing pluses and minuses in your head.

Say you are buying a microcomputer, and want to quantify which machine fits your budget or applications. You lay out information about the type across the top of the spreadsheet. Then you list information about cost, financing, number of users, system maintenance, site preparation, supplies, and training vertically. Develop your own variables based on your own needs.

The accompanying example comes from an analysis of computer graphics equipment by Design and Systems Research, Inc., a Cambridge, Massachusetts strategic planning and marketing firm.

```
DESIGN & SYSTEMS RESEARCH, INC. MICRO-CADD
Cost Benefit Analysis
12 Hour Day, $10/hour Take Home Pay
```

	ASSUMPTNS	2 YEAR AMORT	3 YEAR AMORT
Total System Cost		15000.00	15000.00
CPU			
Workstations			
Plotters			
Total Finance @ RATE >>	.14	3150.00	4200.00
# of users (w/s)	1		
Daily Hours of Use	12		
Hourly Wage Rate	10		
Internal Multiplier	1.5		
Operator/Mgr Cost		93600.00	140400.00
Maintenance %/Year	.1	3000.00	4500.00
Site Prep		3000.00	3000.00
Supplies		2000.00	3000.00
Months Until 1:1 Prod.	2.5		
Fixed Costs/Trainee	2000		
Outside Multiplier	3		
Training/Downtime		21500.00	21500.00
Tax Credits or Other Negatives		.00	.00
Insurance or Other Positives		.00	.00
Total Operation		141250.00	191600.00
Number of Years		2.00	3.00
Cost Per Year		70625.00	63866.67
Yearly Useable Hours		2496.00	2496.00
Console Rate With Labor		28.30	25.59
Hourly Labor Rate		15.00	15.00
Console Rate Without Labor		13.30	10.59
System Cost Ratio		1.89	1.71
Yearly Savings			
PR=2		4255.00	11013.33
PR=3		41695.00	48453.33
PR=4		79135.00	85893.33
PR=5		116575.00	123333.33
% 1st Year Cost Saved			
PR=3		.59	.76
PR=4		1.12	1.34
PR=5		1.65	1.93
Man Years Saved Per Year of Operation			
PR=2		1.50	1.50
PR=3		3.00	3.00
PR=4		4.50	4.50
PR=5		6.00	6.00

34 Grease The Voucher Process

Most busy A/E's will put off submitting
expense vouchers. The procrastination
grows out of the tiresome practice of
filling out voucher forms. When the forms
finally arrive at the accounting
department, they cause problems ranging
from incompleteness to returning to
turning back the pages in the accounting
department. No one in accounting likes to
look backward because one of the
associates is lazy with expense vouchers.

Keep the accounting department happy. Use
a spreadsheet to keep atop your own
expenses. Create a general spreadsheet
format on a micro that works for everyone
in the firm.   As soon as everyone is
inputting their expense information, you
have simplified the task for the
accounting department and sped up the
reimbursement process.

35 Scheduling Bonuses

The Christmas bonus is a tremendous morale booster. It tells a firm's employees that the senior partners have more than ice in their veins. Because of its intrinsic value, senior partners fret over how to plan for the bonuses.

Customize your spreadsheet for bonus distribution. If you use accrual accounting, you can easily estimate how much you need to set aside throughout the year. Your columns can show each employee's salary for the past year, the previous year, past bonuses, and percentages against past salaries.

Since your spreadsheet quickly tells about the level of bonuses, you can adjust it if the financial picture grows bleak at the end of the year. If there are rumors about defections to competitors, you could sweeten the bonus picture for defectors.

36 People & Schedules

You know how many spaces the proposed
project requires. There is the basement,
first floor, second floor, third floor,
fourth floor and fifth floor. You have
outlined services required: measured
drawings, space planning, cost estimating
and asbestos identification.

So how much do you charge for personal
services? Turn to a spreadsheet for the
answer. If you know the spaces and tasks,
then you are prepared to do a fee proposal
breakdown. It will aid your bidding
effort immensely, possibly telling you how
to organize your personnel and for how
long.

Architects & Associates Designers Inc. of
Boston, Massachusetts provides a
spreadsheet example for fee scheduling.
It divides a project into steps, breaks
each step into services, and matches each
breakdown with number of hours per
personnel. Using arithmetic, the
spreadsheet adds hours per person per
step, provides a cost sub-total per step,
and a grand total for the project. Then
use the AIA agreement form 161 for
designated services.

Step 1

	RCS	CTD	NDB	SMM	JHU	PMD	JR	EJM	CL
Site Visit Trip	2	2	2	0	2	2	2	2	2
Measuring	0	20	2	0	16	4	2	2	2
Data Collection - Jacket	0	6	0	0	0	0	0	1	1
Code Review	1	8	4	0	2	0	2	2	2
Draft up Bldg.	0	8	2	0	16	16	2	2	2
Zoning Review	1	4	1	0	1	1	0	0	0
Utility Check	0	4	1	0	2	2	2	1	1
Project Checking	2	6	4	0	4	2	1	1	1
Project Admin.	2	4	2	1	1	1	1	1	1
	8	62	18	1	44	28	12	12	12
	480.00	2170.00	810.00	30.00	1320.00	700.00	600.00	600.00	450.00

Sub-Total: 7160.00

Step 2

	RCS	CTD	NDB	SMM	JHU	PMD	JR	EJM	CL
Writing	1	4	4	0	0	0	2	2	2
Computer Time	0	0	0	4	4	2	0	0	0
	1	4	4	4	4	2	2	2	2
	60.00	140.00	180.00	120.00	120.00	50.00	100.00	100.00	75.00

Sub-Total: 945.00

Step 3

	RCS	CTD	NDB	SMM	JHU	PMD	JR	EJM	CL
Report Writing	2	4	2	1	4	2	2	2	2
Outline Spec	4	2	2	2	2	2	1	2	2
Prelim Cost Est.	4	10	2	2	4	2	1	2	2
Report on M/E	1	1	0	2	2	1	0	1	1
Report on Struct.	1	1	0	2	2	1	1	0	0
Lab Analysis Report	0	1	0	0	2	1	0	0	0
Publication	2	4	2	4	4	4	0	0	0
Office Administ.	2	2	2	2	4	2	0	0	0
	16	25	10	15	24	15	5	7	7
	960.00	875.00	450.00	450.00	720.00	375.00	250.00	350.00	262.50

Sub-Total: 4692.50

37 A Management Direction

Use a spreadsheet to prepare bar charts of tasks versus time. In other words, do your own in-house critical path management without having to buy an expensive dedicated management package.

Spreadsheets give you the capability of revising until you achieve the solution you like. When you finally achieve that solution, print it out for an RFP or photograph for a slide presentation. The example provided by **Todd Lee/FR Clark & Associates** of Boston, Massachusetts was produced on a spreadsheet and enhanced with black drafting tape.

Week : 1 2 3 4 5 6 7 8 9 10 11 12 13 14 15 16 17 18 19 20 21 22 23 24 25 26 27 28 29 30 31 32 33 34 35 36 37 38 39 40 41 42 43 44 45 46 47 48 49 50 51 52

Month :1985 : May : June : July : August : September : October : November : December : January : February : March : April

Date : 6 13 20 27 : 3 10 17 24 : 1 8 15 22 29 : 5 12 19 26 : 2 9 16 23 30 : 7 14 21 28 : 4 11 18 25 : 2 9 16 23 30 : 6 13 20 27 : 3 10 17 24 : 3 10 17 24 31 : 7 14 21 28

1986

PHASE A DATA BASE AND REQUIREMENTS
Task I- Prepare Data Base
  1.1 Introductory Meetings — 1.1 ▬ (1)
  1.2 Existing and additional data — 1.2 ▬ (3)
  1.3 Agency reviews regulations — 1.3 ▬ (3)
  1.4 Indigenous design character — 1.4 ▬ (3)
  1.5 Prototypical design models — 1.5 ▬ (2)
  1.6 Island Data/Workshop One — 1.6 ● (1)

PHASE B PROGRAM DEVELOPMENT
Task II- Tentative Program Development
  II.1 Market potentials — II.1 ▬ (3)
  II.2 Civic and public uses — II.2 ▬ (3)
  II.3 Infrastructure — II.3 ▬ (3)
  II.4- Natural feature, regulation — II.4 ▬ (3)
Task III- Architectural Guidelines
  III.1 Illustrated presentation — III.1 ▬ (3)
  III.2 Design alternatives — III.2 ▬ (2)
Task IV- Board Concurrence and Approval
  IV.1 Review/Approve Tentative Program — IV.1 ▬ (1)
  IV.2 Review/Approve Design Guidelines — IV.2 ▬ (1)

PHASE C PLANNING AND DESIGN
Task V- Prepare Preliminary Master Plan
  V.1 Conceptual Scenarios — V.1 ▬ (3)
  V.2 Conceptual Site Plans — V.2 ▬ (3)
  V.3 Evaluate/Workshop Two — V.3 ● (1)
  V.4 Preliminary Master Plan — V.4 ▬ (8)
  V.5 Approval — V.5 ● (1)
Task VI- Agency Approvals
  VI.1 Formal Reviews — VI.1 ▬ (7)
Task VII- Final Master Plan
  VII.1 Comprehensive Master Plan Document — VII.1 ▬ (7)
  VII.2 Final Approval — VII.2 ● (9)
  VII.3 Camera Ready — VII.3 ▬ 3
  VII.4 Production and Delivery — VII.4 ▬ (3)
  VII.5 Public Presentation — VII.5 ● 1

PHASE D IMPLEMENTATION
Task VIII- Implementation Strategy
  VIII.1 Components — VIII.1 ▬ (2)
  VIII.2 Professional Participation — VIII.2 ▬ (2)

38 Zero In On Fees

The Supreme Court told architects to
create a competitive fee structure. Until
the court moved, architects relied on the
the American Institute of Architects' fee
structure. Now architects must work like
others in the building trade, determining
scope of work, tasks, drawing lists, and
pricing.

Sounds time-consuming! If some computer
jock had not invented the spreadsheet,
that would be a true allegation. A
spreadsheet allows you to lay out all your
data for a project and then compute it
with a few simple key punches. To
establish a fee structure on a
spreadsheet, you should work backward. In
other words, estimate your fee, desired
profit, a consultants' budget, overhead,
and other expenses.

This structure allows you to juggle
variables, negotiate with engineers, look
at profit margins, and control profit.
Spreadsheets and the Supreme Court have
provided the incentive for architects to
walk into a project with eyes on both
finances and design.

Architects & Associated Designers Inc. of
Boston offers the example.

Step 10

	RCS	CTD	NDB/JL	SMM	JHU	PMD	JR	EJM	CL
Shop Drawing Process	4	30	0	0	16	0	2	4	4
Construct. Mtgs. (18) (assume 2 per month @ 4 hrs. total involvement inc. travel, conf., report,)	0 (see above)	72	0	0	0	0	0	0	0
Const. Conf. (9) (assume RCS joins 1 per month @ 2 hrs. total involvement)	18	0 (see above)	0	0	0	0	0	0	0
Conf. w/Consultants (assume 4 @ 2 hrs. each)	0 (see above)	0 (see above)	0	0	0	0	8	8	8 (4 mtgs. @ site)
Cert. of Payment Process	5 (1/2 hr. ea.)	10 (1 hr. ea.)	0	0	0	0	1 (conf.)	1 (conf.)	1 (conf.)
Const. Monitor/Inspt. 36 Visits (assumes 1 day/wk. other than bi-weekly mtg, 4 hr. total involvement ea.)	0 (see above)	144	0	0	0	0	0	0	0
Site visits by Consult. (assume 3 hr/ea total)	0	0	0	0	0	0	6 (2 visits)	6 (2 visits)	6 (2 visits)
	27	256	0	0	16	0	17	19	19
	1620.00	8960.00	0.00	0.00	480.00	0.00	850.00	950.00	712.50

Sub-Total: 13572.50

Step 11

	RCS	CTD	NDB/JL	SMM	JHU	PMD	JR	EJM	CL
Site Visit/Travel	4	4	0	0	0	0	1	1	1
Punch List	4	4	0	0	0	0	2	2	2
Administrative	4	4	0	0	0	0	0	0	0
Final Punch List w/Contractor	4	4	0	0	0	0	0	0	0
	16	16	0	0	0	0	3	3	3
	960.00	560.00	0.00	0.00	0.00	0.00	150.00	150.00	112.50

Sub-Total: 1932.50

39 Counting BTUs

A municipality is spending thousands of dollars on energy. The elected officials are outraged. They demand that every town employee take a pledge to turn off lights, turn down thermostats in their rooms, and start wearing sweaters. The employees rebel.

Isn't a systematic heat loss analysis of suspected energy leaks more realistic? **J. Kenneth Fraser & Associates** of Rensselaer, New York has a solution to this dilemma. It uses a spreadsheet to analyze BTU levels, giving sub-totals for various spaces. Within those spaces, the spreadsheet accounts for material thermal coefficients and dimensions.

Fraser provided this example of a heat loss calculation for pump station.

```
HEAT LOSS CALCULATIONS

     11-Mar-85

JOB NO:
CLIENT:        TOWN OF
PROJECT:       PUMP STATION

-------------------------------------------------------------
SPACE            PUMP RM     GEN       LAV    STORAGE    TOTAL

EXT WALL             112      30        5         5       152
HEIGHT                13      13       13        13        52
GROSS WALL AREA     1456     390       65        65      1976
WINDOW AREA          144      18        6         0       168
DOOR AREA             42       0        0         0        42
NET WALL AREA       1270     372       59        65      1766
ROOF AREA           1148     200       40        40      1428
-------------------------------------------------------------
HEAT LOSS BTU/H    54855   10584     1727      1193     68359

-------------------------------------------------------------
PUMP ROOM        AREA      U        DELTA T  CFH     HEAT LOSS

FLOOR             112                  70              5040
WINDOW            144     0.6          70              6048
DOOR               42     0.6          70              1764
VALL             1270     0.11         70              9779
ROOF             1148     0.05         70              4018
MECH VENT                              70                 0
INFILTRATION    14924     1.5          70     22386   28206
                                            SUBTOTAL   54855
-------------------------------------------------------------
```

40 Minimize Oversights

The never-ending task of project estimates
is one of those evil A/E necessities. It
requires long hours and meticulous care.
One mistake could halt a project. Too
many oversights, and it will cost your
firm money.

From beneath the arc of electricity comes
the spreadsheet to the rescue. **Architects
& Associated Designers, Inc.** of Boston
have such a spreadsheet. It divides every
project into parts, which are themselves
divided into everything under the sun from
agreement forms, to sewer systems, to
railroad work. Whatever will go out to
bid or requires A/E time should find a
home on the spreadsheet.

Into the information cells in the
spreadsheet goes costs, and out at the
bottom of the sheet comes reality --
"total estimated cost." Spreadsheets only
require organization and information
collection. Your own programmed formulas
do the rest.

	A	B	C	D	E	F	G	H	I	J	K	L	M
1	Architects & Associated Designers, Inc./A&AD												
2	286 Congress Street, Boston, Massachusetts 02210-1052												
3	Telephone 617-482-7502 Owip 1200 Telex 951131												
4													
5	Remarks:												
6	Based on 8 month/32 week duration				Rate/hr	Rate/day	Rate/week						
7	Labor:(incl. labor benefits)				18.75	150.00	750.00	Assume:					
8	Carpenter:(incl. labor benefits)				25.00	200.00	1,000.00	General Contractor has labor and carpenter trades.					
9	Mechanical:(incl. labor benefits)				25.00	200.00	1,000.00	All new utilities					
10	Subcontractor:				30.00	240.00	1,250.00	13,722 square feet without basement (± 2,500 square feet).					
11													
12	Description	CSI No.	Labor					Material				Equipment Rental	
13			Unit	No. Units	Unit Cost	Total Cost		Unit	No. Units	Unit Cost	Total Cost	Unit	No. Units	Unit Co:
14													
15	Division 0 - BIDDING AND												
16	CONTRACT REQUIREMENTS												
17													
18	Pre-Bid Information	00010				0.00					0.00		
19	Instructions to Bidders	00100				0.00					0.00		
20	Information Available to Bidders	00200				0.00					0.00		
21	Bid/Tender Forms	00300				0.00					0.00		
22	Supplements to Bid/Tender Forms	00400				0.00					0.00		
23	Agreement Forms	00500				0.00					0.00		
24	Bonds and Certificates	00600				0.00	1/s		1	15,000.00	15,000.00		
25	General Conditions of the Contract	00700	1/s	1	33,500.00	33,500.00					0.00		
26	Supplementary Conditions	00800	1/s	1	2,000.00	2,000.00					0.00		
27	Drawings Index	00850				0.00					0.00		
28	Addenda and Modifications	00900	1/s	1	2,000.00	2,000.00					0.00		
29	Total Division 0					37,500.00					15,000.00		
30													
31	Division 1 - GENERAL												
32	REQUIREMENTS												
33													
34	Summary of Work	01010				0.00					0.00		
35	Allowances	01020				0.00	1/s		1	1,000.00	1,000.00		
36	Special Project Procedures	01030				0.00					0.00	1/s	1	5,00
37													
38	Coordination	01040				0.00					0.00		
39	Project Coordination	01041	mw	64	700.00	44,800.00					0.00	1/s	1	2,80
40	Mechanical and Electrical Coord	01042	mw	4	1,250.00	5,000.00					0.00		
41	Cutting and Patching	01045	mw	10	750.00	7,500.00					0.00		
42													
43	Field Engineering	01050	mw	1	1,000.00	1,000.00	1/s		1	1,500.00	1,500.00		
44													
45	Regulatory Requirements	01060				0.00					0.00		
46	Building Codes and Fees (Permits)	01061	md	15	200.00	3,000.00	1/s		1	9,600.00	9,600.00		
47													
48	Abbreviations and Symbols	01070				0.00					0.00		
49	Identification Systems	01080	mw	1	1,000.00	1,000.00	1/s		1	500.00	500.00		
50	Alternates/Alternatives	01100				0.00					0.00		
51	Measurement and Payment	01150				0.00					0.00		
52	Project Mtgs 2hrs 32 mtgs @ $25	01200	mh	64	25.00	1,600.00					0.00		
53	Submittals	01300	1/s	1	2,000.00	2,000.00	1/s		1	800.00	800.00		
54	Quality Control	01400	1/s	1	1,000.00	1,000.00					0.00		
55													

41 Homespun Economics

"Where have all the economists gone?"
asked the A/E.

"To Washington. To Washington," chimed the
local government authorities.

"But why?" retorted the angered A/E. "To
tell Congress how to spend foreign aid.
It's more exciting than telling us how to
plan our sewer debt payments. We'd join
them, if only we knew something about
economics."

Seems no one enjoys project economics.
Too bad for A/E's, because they end up
assuming that responsibility for most
public works projects. Solving cash flow
and other financial problems falls on the
shoulders of design-oriented A/E's. Don't
worry, though. Use your spreadsheet. J.
Kenneth Fraser & Associates of Rensselaer,
New York offer an example that analyzes a
client's cash flow over a 30-year period.
It includes assumptionns about all
factors, from interest rates and revenue,
to costs and expenses.

FILE: FINANCE 1

J. KENNETH FRASER AND ASSOCIATES, P.C.
HYDROELECTRIC CASHFLOW SPREADSHEET

CENTRAL HUDSON HYDROELECTRIC DEVELOPMENT PROJECT

5 YR. DEP. ADJUST.	0
18 YR. DEP ADJUST.	0
CONSTR. COST ADJUSTMENT	0

ASSUMPTIONS		COSTS	
INTEREST RATE	0.14	CONSTRUCTION COST	262,900
INFLATION RATE 1	0.07	CONTINGENCIES	26,290
INFLATION RATE 2	0.00	ENGINEERING,LEGAL,FINANCE	72,298
DEBT RATIO	1.00	INT. DURING CONSTRUCTION	25,304
DISCOUNT RATE	0.10	FINANCE CHARGE (3%)	0
INVESTMENT TAX CREDIT	0.10	WATER INSURANCE (5%)	0
ENERGY TAX CREDIT	0.11	TOTAL PROJECT COST	386,792
LOAN TERM	15		
CONSTRUCTION TERM	1		

REVENUE		CALCULATIONS	
POWER PRODUCED (KWH/YEAR)	900,000	5 YR. DEPRECIABLE AMOUNT	181,500
MIN. RATE/KWH	0.06	PER YEAR	36,300
GROSS ANNUAL REVENUE	54,000	18 YR. DEPRECIABLE AMOUNT	107,690
		PER YEAR	5,983
EXPENSES		ITC BASE	289,190
		ETC BASE	289,190
ANN'L O.&M. & REPLACEMENT	3,000	STATE TAX RATE	10%
ANNUAL ROYALTY-6%	3,240	FEDERAL TAX RATE	46%

ANALYSIS W/O SALVAGE
----
30 YR. P.W. NET CASH FLOW   239,028

CASH FLOW NEXT PAGE--------->

ASSUMPTIONS: ROYALTY TO MUNICIPALITY 6% OF YEARLY REVENUE
             INVESTMENT TAX CREDIT EXISTS
             ENERGY TAX CREDIT EXISTS

42 One Step Ahead

And the old adage says: "Times flies when you're having fun." Unfortunately, this adage runs counter to the wisdom of time management. That wisdom demands that you wring out as much effort as possible from every second. To find a compromise between the old adage and new wisdom, A/Es should take advantage of spreadsheets.

Architects & Associated Designers, Inc. of Boston has a firm-tailored spreadsheet for its timetable. It has columns to list name, days of the week, and total hours per project. At the bottom of the spreadsheet, the internal calculator of the spreadsheet offers up totals per day and per week.

Period Ending   24 May 1986

Project Number	Project Name and Description	Phase	Sun 18	Mon 19	Tues 20	Wed 21	Thur 22	Fri 23	Sat 24	Total Hours
85112	Lawrence Airport – with Chuck DiPerri	7.01					0.25	1.50		1.75
85112	Lawrence Airport – Shekar	7.01					0.75	0.50		1.25
85112	Lawrence Airport – Field Order	7.42						0.25		0.25
										0.00
85170	BAC/YOU – Base Plans onto Mac	3.01		0.50			1.25	0.25		2.00
85170	BAC/YOU – Ted McAlarney Interview	3.01					0.75			0.75
85170	BAC/YOU – Ed Fischer Interview	3.01					1.00			1.00
85170	BAC/YOU – Travel	3.01			1.00					1.00
85170	BAC/YOU – Site Visit	3.01			2.00					2.00
85170	BAC/YOU – Scheduling	3.29			1.00	0.50				1.50
85170	BAC/YOU – Engineering Coordination	3.02						0.75		0.75
85170	BAC/YOU – "Quick Sections"	3.21						0.25		0.25
										0.00
86159P	BRA Infill Housing Development Proposal Development	0.94		1.50						1.50
										0.00
86113	New Bedford Airport/Term. Expan. Fee Scheduling	4.01		0.50	0.25					0.75
85167	New Bedford Airport/Equip. Stor. Bldg. Fee Scheduling	4.01		0.50		0.25				0.75
85167	New Bedford Airport/Equip. Stor. Bldg. (w/ E&K)	4.01				1.00	0.50			1.50
85167	New Bedford Airport/Equip. Stor. Bldg. Cost Estimate	4.32					0.25	1.25		1.50
										0.00
85109	126 High Street	0.96		0.50						0.50
										0.00
86158P	Pomeroy School – John Stainton	0.94		0.25		1.00				1.25
86158P	Pomeroy School Presentation	0.94						0.75	3.00	3.75
86136	Hyde Park YMCA window replacement	1.07				2.50				2.50
86139	FIRST Inc. Dormer Addition (site visit)	1.07				2.00				2.00
86140	Dorchester YMCA – Mary Broemel (BRA)	6.01		0.25			0.25			0.50
86134	Hope House	3.02		0.25						0.25
86134	Hope House – Frank Cogliano	3.01		0.50	0.75	0.25				1.50
86134	Hope House – Conference with Client	3.01			2.00					2.00
86134	Hope House – Joe McConagle/Jim Regan	3.01					0.50			0.50
86135	Dorchester House Automatic Doors	1.07				2.00				2.00
86010	Tom Friedman (Computer Book)	0.94		0.25						0.25
86000	Macintosh Seminar – "What do you do after you double-click"	0.93		3.00						3.00
86000	Office Manual	0.87					0.75	1.25		2.00
86000	Computer Maintenance	0.87			0.75					0.75
86000	Office/Project Scheduling (with JHU)	0.87		1.50	0.75			1.25		3.50
86000	Staff Meeting – Marketing	0.89		0.75			0.50			1.25
86000	Staff Meeting – General (scheduling)	0.89		0.75						0.75
86000	Computer Aquisition Preparation	0.94			0.25	0.75	1.25			2.25
86000	Computer Aquisition Meeting with Linda Swenson	0.94					1.25			1.25
Total Hours			0.00	11.00	8.75	10.25	9.25	8.00	3.00	**50.25**

Architects & Associated Designers Inc./A&AD

43 Zoning Plays

The spreadsheet has the power to attack zoning. It will detail building type and provide a selection of possibilities suitable for a particular location. For example, **Todd Lee/FR Clark & Associates** of Boston uses a spreadsheet to determine how to take advantage of unused air rights around and above buildings.

The spreadsheet turned a theoretical scenario to test against zoning criteria. Among important factors analyzed were building floor space.

Governing criteria:
Add 2 floors of Office @15,000 sf. With Retail @ 15,000sf, Residential fills remainder of allowable FAR. Parking as required on two levels underground.

	(a) Program	(b) :Total :Area : sf	(c) :Min.# :Park'g :Spaces	(d) :Min. # :Loading :Bays	(e) ::EST. CONST. COST ::Unit (1) ::Cost	(f) :Total :Cost :
1.1	RETAIL :	13,690 :	15 :	1 ::	$50 :	$684,500 :
2.1	RESIDENTIAL :	:	:	na ::	:	:
2.2	24 - 1 BR :24 @ 750(1.15)= :	:	:	::	:	:
2.3	:	17,250 :	:	::	$55 :	$948,750 :
2.4	80 - 2 BR :80 @ 950(1.15)= :	:	:	::	:	:
2.5	:	78,660 :	:	::	$55 :	$4,326,300 :
2.6	:---------------- :			::	:------------:	
2.7	92 Units :	95,910 :	92 :	::	:	$5,275,050 :
3.1	OFFICE :	:	:	1 ::	:	:
	General :	20,000 :	22 :	::	$70 :	$1,400,000 :
	Medical :	10,000 :	20 :	::	$70 :	$700,000 :
	:----------------:------:			::	:------------:	
	:	30,000 :	42 :	::	:	$2,100,000 :
4.1	PARKING :	:	:	::	:	:
4.2	Surface @ :	0 :	40 :	::	$0 :	$0 :
4.3	@300 sf :	in site costs :	:	::	:	:
4.4	Level 1 below:	:	55 :	::	$10,000 :	$547,167 :
4.5	@350 sf :	19,151 :	:	::	:	:
4.6	Level 2 below:	:	55 :	na ::	$10,000 :	$547,167 :
4.7	@350 sf :	19,151 :	:	::	:	:
4.8	Total Parking:	38,302 :	149 :	::	:	$1,094,333 :
5.1	SITE COSTS say=	19,600 :	:	::	$20 :	$392,000
6.1	CONSTRUCTION : TOTALS	177,902 :	149 :	2 ::	$53.66 :	$9,545,883 :
7.1	F.A.R. USED	139,600	-(not incl parking)			
7.2	MAX. ALLOW.FAR :	139,600 :	:	::	:	:
	:-----------------:					
7.3	F.A.R. NOT USED	0				

NOTES:
(1) In general, unit costs used are those proposed by Associates, however the experience of three seperate structural engineers (two with nearby Mass. Ave. experience) suggests that underground parking, involving underpinning adjacent structures, sheeting the site, and Red Line complexities, make a $30 to $40 psf x 350 sf = say $10,000, cost projection more prudent.

(2) Efficiency of residential units assumed at 115% net to gross including lobby, corridors, and mechanicals.

44 Early Organization

What's the best use of your staffs' time? That's the right question to ask at the beginning of every week. Four to put out that fire. Two to finish off that RFP. Three to work on new drawings for the old church.

When you know all that, where do you store the information? Sure, you assign tasks. But do you tell your staff exactly how many hours for each particular staff? It's amazing what happens when people know they have only three hours to complete a project. They do what needs to be done. On the other hand, some projects seem to float on some ethereal substance.

Architects & Associated Designers, Inc. offer this spreadsheet solution. At the beginning of each week, staff members receive a schedule with project no., status and project name plus the amount of time required for their contribution. At the end of the week, the schedule serves as a productivity guide, since it can be matched against timesheets.

Architects & Associated Designers, Inc./A&AD
286 Congress Street, Boston, Massachusetts 02210-1053
Telephone 617-482-7502 Qwip 1200 Telex 951131

WEEKLY SCHEDULE
January 27-31, 1986

Project No.	Status	Project Name	RCS	NDB	JCL	CTD	SMM	JHU	PMD	JKO	GED	AR
82118	™	ASTRA	1	8					4			
83104	*	Carriage House	2	2								
83144	™	Bildman CM	1									
83225	*	NDEA Coordination 1985				1						
84150	™	Arne Hill								0.5		
84163	*	Quincy School				0						
84164	*	Dorchester C.C.						0				
84167	*	FIRST, Inc.				0						
84170	*	Dorchester YMCA					0					
84176	*	ECSCS 2	1					4				
84196	'	Monadnock				4						
84200	'	VA Convert Theatre	2	2		12				8	3	
84214	'	Tuckpointing	1				2					
85104	*	Abraham School				1						
85105	'	New Bedford Term. Renov.	2		6			8				
85109	*	126 High Street	4	4			2					
85112	'	Lawrence Airport	1			4						
85116	*	Y.E.S.				0						
85119	*	NDEA Coordination 1986	0			0						
85132	'	VA C.A.T. Scan	0			0						
85141	'	VA Morgue Brooklyn	2							2		
85142	'	ADP Phase 2	0				0					
85143	'	VA Storage Alcoves	4			8	1	8	28	4		
85152	™	Bildman / Killington	4							2		
85163	™	Swensrude Residence	8			2	35	4				
85167P	*	New Bedford Storage Bldg	0					0				
85170P	*	BAC/YOU	6	12		4						
85172P	*	126 High Street Rend.	0	0								
85173	™	Keliher Group	0.5					2				
85177	™	Linnell	4	4					8			
85179	'	Cement LaFarge	2		6							
85189	*	Cedarville Village	6									
85182	™	ASTRA Vault				0						
85183	™	ASTRA Laboratory	1		12	12						
86000	*	General Administration	10			2				11.5	5	4
86000	*	Scheduling	1			4						
86000	*	Accounting								12		
86010	*	Marketing									32	
86111	*	21 Melville Avenue	1					6	8			
86113	*	New Bedford Term. Expan.	4		1			8				
Total			68 5	0| 32	0| 25	0| 54	0| 40	0| 40	0| 48	0| 40	0| 40	0| 4	0|

45 End Number Chugging

Structural analysis. It's a regular obligation for every engineer. Not many engineers relish computing bending capacities, hydrostatic load factors, shear and torsion, and uniform dead load. Nevertheless, whenever you design a large public works structure, you've got to know all these parameters.

At **J. Kenneth Fraser & Associates** of Rensselaer, New York the engineers don't like structural analysis any more than the next A/E. The Fraser engineers, however, don't spend much time fussing. They've created a simple spreadsheet that calculates the major parameters for structural concrete.

Fraser provides an example of typical spreadsheet analysis:

```
J. KENNETH FRASER & ASSOCIATES, P.C.       STRUCTURAL CONCRETE
22 HIGH STREET, RENSSELAER, N.Y. 12144     DESIGN SPREADSHEET

BY:JFB                    DATE:4/7/86       SHEET NO.:1
CHKD. BY:JFB              DATE:4/10/86
SUBJECT:INTAKE BAY - NORTH WALL
==================================================================
 DESIGN PARAMETERS                  LOAD DATA (KIPS)
CONCRETE  Fc (ksi)            3.5 HYDROSTATIC DESIGN ELEV.     100
STEEL Fy (ksi)                 60 COMPONENT ELEVATION           80
PHI BENDING CAPACITY REDUCT   0.9 FACTORED HYDROSTATIC LOAD  1.7472
PHI SHEAR AND TORSION        0.85 UNIFORM DEAD LOAD           1.248
DEAD LOAD FACTOR              1.4 UNIFORM LIVE LOAD           1.248
LIVE LOAD FACTOR              1.7 FACTORED LOAD Wu            2.496
HYDROSTATIC LOAD FACTOR.      1.4
------------------------------------------------------------------
 GEOMETRY                           BEAM TYPE   DESIGNATION
b (IN.)                        12      SIMPLE         1
d (IN.)                        21      FIXED          2
SPAN (FT.)                     20
BEAM TYPE (1 OR 2)              2
BAR SIZE(#)                     8
------------------------------------------------------------------
 ANALYSIS                    +Mu     -Mu      Vu  (ALL UNITS KIPS
UNIFORM LOADS                41.6    83.2    25.0        & FEET)
HYDROSTATIC LOADS            14.8    34.9    12.2
TOTAL                        56.4   118.1    37.2
------------------------------------------------------------------
STEEL CALCULATIONS

                               REBAR
                   /------------------------------\
Mu DESIGN     As   SIZE   NUMBER   AREA   SPACING   Mu FURN.
     118     1.32    8      2      0.79      6.0      146.0
     118     1.32    6      3      0.44      4.0      122.4
     118     1.32   11      1      1.56     12.0      144.2
      56     0.61    8      1      0.79     12.0       73.8
      56     0.61    6      2      0.44      6.0       82.1
      56     0.61   10      1      1.27     12.0      117.9
      NA      NA     8     NA      0.79      NA         NA

SHEAR REQUIREMENTS

    Vu/PHI     Vc      Vs  BAR SIZE     Av   SPACING
     43.8     29.8    13.9      4      0.40    10.5
```

46 Sizing Space

Many A/E projects demand calculation of
gross to net areas for individual spaces
or entire buildings. Some government
agencies require that individual spaces
stay within 10 percent "spread of program
areas." If you are designing with CAD,
then you have automatic dimensioning and
database capabilities.

If you are without CAD, you could
substitute a spreadsheet. The
spreadsheet makes possible multiplication
of room dimensions, addition,
subtraction, sub-totals, percentages, and
gross to net counts. When you design
changes, you enter new data and the
spreadsheet automatically recalculates.

47 Elevated Insights

If you are an elevator consultant,
financial analysis of elevator operations
versus overall building cost is critical.
If you are an A/E with an elevator
department, the same hold true. With a
spreadsheet, you can turn this very
important and difficult analysis into a
relatively easy task.

From a spreadsheet, you will learn the
cost-benefits based on the cost of
building envelope, number of floors, and
area per floor. Even if you advise
against numerous elevators, you will be
able to encourage your client to build
staggered work hours into a lease to
coordinate elevator service -- and
minimize building costs.

48 Fire Prevention

Keep the fire department at the firehouse.
Don't spend hours worrying about a
sprinkler system design. Use a spreadsheet
to analyze a system before you build it.
Consider all the variables -- elevation,
pipe length, pipe diameter, municipal
code, etc. -- and compute how to build a
sprinkler system that is legal, and works.

J. Kenneth Fraser & Associates of
Rensselaer, New York provides an example:

FILE B87FL2S

BUILDING 87 SPRINKLER ANALYSIS - SECOND FLOOR SOUTH EAST

MINIMUM DENSITY AT END HEAD OVER 42 SQ. FT. = 0.350

K	Pt	Pn	q	Q	I.D.	length	Pf	Pe	Pv	Ref.Pt.	Elev.	coeff.	Lp	Lf	Ftgs.
5.56	7.00	7.00	14.71	14.71	1.00	6	0.78	0.00		Ref. Pt.	44	100	0	6	T
5.27	7.78	7.78	14.71	14.71	1.00	.				Ref. Pt.	44				
SUMMARY, TYP. HEAD NO RISER										Equiv. K value for branch					
5.27	7.78	7.78	14.71	14.71	1.00	11	1.43	0.00		Ref. Pt.	44	100	6	5	T
5.27	9.22	9.12	15.92	30.63	1.25	8	1.37	0.43	0.10	Ref. Pt.	43	100	2	6	T
9.23	11.02	11.02	14.71	14.71	1.00	9	1.17	0.00		Ref. Pt.	44	100	4	5	T
SUMMARY, TYP 2 HEAD-6' LATERAL										Equiv. K value for branch					
5.27	7.78	7.78	14.71	14.71	1.00	9	1.17	0.00		Ref. Pt.	44	100	4	5	T
5.27	8.96	8.86	15.69	30.40	1.25	8	1.35	0.43	0.10	Ref. Pt.	43	100	2	6	T
9.28	10.74	10.74	14.71	14.71	1.00	5		0.43		Ref. Pt.	43	100	5	8	T
SUMMARY, TYP. 2 HEAD-4' LATERAL										Equiv. K value for branch					
9.23	11.02	11.02	14.71	14.71	1.25	5	0.85	0.00		Ref. Pt.	43	100	5	0	T
9.23	11.87	11.66	31.52	62.15	1.50	13	3.38	0.00	0.21	Ref. Pt.	43	100	5	8	T
15.91	15.25	15.25	15.25							Ref. Pt.	43				
SUMMARY, WEST BRANCH JT.1										Equiv. K value for branch					
5.27	7.78	7.78	14.71	14.71	1.00	5	0.65	0.00		Ref. Pt.	43	100	5	0	T
5.27	8.43	8.33	15.22	29.93	1.25	11	1.80	0.00	0.10	Ref. Pt.	43	100	5	6	T
9.36	10.24	10.24	14.71							Ref. Pt.	43				
SUMMARY, NORTH BRANCH JT. 1										Equiv. K value for branch					
34.55	15.25	15.25	134.93	134.93	2.00	12	3.23	0.00		JOINT 1 Ref. Pt.	43	100	2	10	T
31.39	15.25	15.25								Ref. Pt.	43				
SUMMARY, WEST SIDE JT.2										Equiv. K value for branch					
5.27	7.78	7.78	14.71	14.71	1.00	10	0.65	0.00		Ref. Pt.	43	100	5	6	T
5.27	8.43	8.33	15.22	29.93	1.25	5	1.64	0.00	0.10	Ref. Pt.	43	100	4	6	T
9.43	10.07	10.07	14.71							Ref. Pt.	43				
SUMMARY, EAST SIDE JT.2										Equiv. K value for branch					
40.82	18.48	18.48	175.48	175.48	2.50	20	2.95	0.00		JOINT 2 Ref. Pt.	43	100	8	12	T
37.90	21.43	18.48								Ref. Pt.	44				
SUMMARY, SOUTH SIDE JT. 3										Equiv. K value for branch					
5.27	7.78	7.78	14.71	14.71	1.00	6	0.78	0.00	0.10	Ref. Pt.	44	100	6	6	T
5.27	8.56	8.47	15.34	30.05	1.25	11	1.81	0.43	0.10	Ref. Pt.	43	100	5	8	T
5.27	10.81	10.61	17.18	47.23	1.50	11	1.72	0.20	0.20	Ref. Pt.	43	100	3	8	T
13.34	12.53							0.00		Ref. Pt.	43				
SUMMARY, EAST SIDE JT.4										Equiv. K value for branch					
5.27	18.48														
5.10	8.30	7.78	14.71	14.71	1.00	4	0.52	0.00		Ref. Pt.	43	100	4 Fitt.		T
SUMMARY, SOUTH SIDE JT.4										Equiv. K value for branch					

88

49 Price Deduction

Ever wonder how to rid yourself of the "cost-estimate" brain drain? **J. Kenneth Fraser and Associates** consulting engineers of Rensselaer, New York used a spreadsheet on a street improvement project. The project called for dust control, tree removal, stump removal, excavation, road stabilization, and stone curb resetting, among a dozen other jobs. Fraser viewed this task as nothing more than a calculation.

Firm engineers took advantage of the listing, multiplying, and additional functions of a spreadsheet. They listed -- from left to right -- item number, job description, estimated quantity, units per dollar, and amount in columns. As the engineers entered each item, the spreadsheet automatically tallied. When all the information was entered, it represented the sub-totals and total for the overall project.

```
CITY OF FAIRVIEW, FAIRVIEW COUNTY, NEW YORK          J. KENNETH FRASER & ASSOCIATES, P.C.
CONTRACT NO. 2 - MISC. STREET IMPROVEMENTS           CONSULTING ENGINEERS
                                                     22 HIGH STREET
ENGINEER'S ESTIMATE                                  RENSSELAER, NEW YORK  12144

==============================================================================================
   ITEM NO.           DESCRIPTION                 EST QTY   UNIT   UNIT $    AMOUNT
==============================================================================================
   01562      DUST CONTROL - CALCIUM CHLORIDE         2     TON    200.00      400.00
   02111.03   TREE REMOVAL (25"-36")                  2     EACH   175.00      350.00
   02111.06   STUMP REMOVAL (25"-36")                 2     EACH   250.00      500.00
   02200.01   EXCAVATION                          2,500     C.Y.    10.00    25000.00
   02200.02   GRANULAR BEDDING                       60     C.Y.    15.00      900.00
   02200.03   SELECT FILL                            90     C.Y.    15.00     1350.00
   02200.04   RUN OF BANK GRAVEL                     50     C.Y.    15.00      750.00
 * 02222      ROCK EXCAVATION (1)                     5     C.Y.    30.00      150.00
   02272.01   ROAD STABILIZATION FABRIC           4,800     S.Y.     1.50     7200.00
   02510.01   CONCRETE SIDEWALKS & DRIVEWAYS        100     S.Y.    35.00     3500.00
 * 02510.02   ADDITIONAL FIRST CLASS CONCRETE         5     C.Y.   200.00     1000.00
   02511      GRAVEL SUB-BASE                     1,600     C.Y.    10.00    16000.00
   02513.01   ASPHALT CONCRETE - TYPE 5 SHIM COURSE 120     TON     50.00     6000.00
   02513.05   NEW BITUM. SDWLKS, & DRVWYS - 2-1/2" THICK  75 S.Y.   15.00     1125.00
   02513.06   NEW BITUM. ROADWAYS - 3-1/2" THICK  4,800     S.Y.     7.50    36000.00
   02513.07   BITUM. PAVEMENT OVERLAY 1"-1-1/2" THICK 14,000 S.Y.    3.50    49000.00
   02528      RE-SET EXISTING STONE CURB            525     L.F.    10.00     5250.00
   02529      PRECAST CONCRETE CURB               1,525     L.F.    16.00    24400.00
   02575.01   CONDITIONING EXISTING PAVEMENT     14,000     S.Y.     0.65     9100.00
   02575.02   PAVEMENT FABRIC                    14,000     L.F.     1.50    21000.00
   02577      PAVEMENT MARKINGS                     900     L.F.     2.00     1800.00
   02721.01   CATCH BASINS, FRAMES AND GRATES         3     EACH  2000.00     6000.00
   02722.12   12" STORM SEWER PIPE                   60     L.F.    50.00     3000.00
   02722.18   18" STORM SEWER PIPE                  320     L.F.    30.00     9600.00
   02723      SUBSURFACE DRAIN                    2,600     L.F.     8.00    20800.00
   02730.01   MANHOLES, FRAMES AND COVERS             3     EACH  2000.00     6000.00
   02930      TURF ESTABLISHMENT                      1     L.S.  2000.00     2000.00
   02950      LANDSCAPING-PLANTING (2-1/2" CALIPER)   2     EACH   250.00      500.00
----------------------------------------------------------------------------------------------
                                                          TOTAL         $258,675.00
```

50 Bid Tabulation

Using the spreadsheet in the previous example, you can create a bid tabulation. You keep the items, quantities, and units the same. But you substitute the engineer's estimated unit prices with the contractors' bid prices. At the end of the bid tabulation, the spreadsheet calculates the minimum, maximum, and average bids that are then used for future engineering estimates.

The process is useful in negotiating special unit prices with the low bidder for lump sum projects and alternatives that might be wildly out of line with the mainstream of bidding.

The example is from **J. Kenneth Fraser & Associates** of Rensselaer, New York:

				ACME CONSTRUCTION, INC. 107 MAIN STREET FAIRVIEW, NY 10101 5% BID BOND		JONES CONSTRUCTION CO. 34 LAKE AVENUE FAIRVIEW, NY 10101 5% BID BOND				

CONTRACTOR

BID SECURITY

ITEM NO.	DESCRIPTION	QUANTITY	UNIT	UNIT $	TOTAL $	UNIT $	TOTAL $	MINIMUM	MAXIMUM	AVERAGE
01562	DUST CONTROL - CALCIUM CHLORIDE	2	TON	100.00	200.00	400.00	800.00	100.00	400.00	250.00
02111.03	TREE REMOVAL (25"-36")	2	EACH	250.00	500.00	150.00	300.00	150.00	250.00	200.00
02111.06	STUMP REMOVAL (25"-36")	2	EACH	100.00	200.00	600.00	1200.00	100.00	600.00	350.00
02200.01	EXCAVATION	2,500	C.Y.	8.50	21250.00	12.00	30000.00	8.50	12.00	10.25
02200.02	GRANULAR BEDDING	60	C.Y.	20.00	1200.00	14.00	840.00	14.00	20.00	17.00
02200.03	SELECT FILL	90	C.Y.	20.00	1800.00	8.00	720.00	8.00	20.00	14.00
02200.04	RUN OF BANK GRAVEL	50	C.Y.	20.00	1000.00	8.00	400.00	8.00	20.00	14.00
02222	ROCK EXCAVATION (1)	5	C.Y.	30.00	150.00	30.00	150.00	30.00	30.00	30.00
02272.01	ROAD STABILIZATION FABRIC	4,800	S.Y.	1.50	7200.00	1.00	4800.00	1.00	1.50	1.25
02510.01	CONCRETE SIDEWALKS & DRIVEWAYS	100	S.Y.	36.00	3600.00	35.00	3500.00	35.00	36.00	35.50
02510.02	ADDITIONAL FIRST CLASS CONCRETE	5	C.Y.	300.00	1500.00	100.00	500.00	100.00	300.00	200.00
02511	GRAVEL SUB-BASE	1,600	C.Y.	10.00	16000.00	14.00	22400.00	10.00	14.00	12.00
02513.01	ASPHALT CONCRETE - TYPE 5 SHIM COURSE	120	TON	50.00	6000.00	45.00	5400.00	45.00	50.00	47.50
02513.05	NEW BITUM. SDWLKS, & DRVWYS - 2-1/2" THICK	75	S.Y.	15.00	1125.00	10.00	750.00	10.00	15.00	12.50
02513.06	NEW BITUM. ROADWAYS - 3-1/2" THICK	4,800	S.Y.	7.50	36000.00	8.00	38400.00	7.50	8.00	7.75
02513.07	BITUM. PAVEMENT OVERLAY 1"-1-1/2" THICK	14,000	S.Y.	3.50	49000.00	2.80	39200.00	2.80	3.50	3.15
02528	RE-SET EXISTING STONE CURB	525	L.F.	10.00	5250.00	9.00	4725.00	9.00	10.00	9.50
02529	PRECAST CONCRETE CURB	1,525	L.F.	16.00	24400.00	15.50	23637.50	15.50	16.00	15.75
02575.01	CONDITIONING EXISTING PAVEMENT	14,000	S.Y.	0.65	9100.00	0.60	8400.00	0.60	0.65	0.63
02575.02	PAVEMENT FABRIC	14,000	S.Y.	1.75	24500.00	1.55	21700.00	1.55	1.75	1.65
02577	PAVEMENT MARKINGS	900	L.F.	2.50	2250.00	1.65	1485.00	1.65	2.50	2.08
02721.01	CATCH BASINS, FRAMES AND GRATES	3	EACH	2000.00	6000.00	2000.00	6000.00	2000.00	2000.00	2000.00
02722.12	12" STORM SEWER PIPE	60	L.F.	60.00	3600.00	50.00	3000.00	50.00	60.00	55.00
02722.18	18" STORM SEWER PIPE	320	L.F.	25.00	8000.00	38.00	12160.00	25.00	38.00	31.50
02723	SUBSURFACE DRAIN	2,600	L.F.	8.00	20800.00	7.00	18200.00	7.00	8.00	7.50
02730.01	MANHOLES, FRAMES AND COVERS	3	EACH	2000.00	6000.00	2500.00	7500.00	2000.00	2500.00	2250.00
02930	TURF ESTABLISHMENT	1	L.S.	2000.00	2000.00	3500.00	3500.00	2000.00	3500.00	2750.00
02950	LANDSCAPING-PLANTING (2-1/2" CALIPER)	2	EACH	500.00	1000.00	225.00	450.00	225.00	500.00	362.50

TOTAL AMOUNT BID: $259,625.00 $260,117.50

51 Financially Tidy

The spreadsheet used in the two previous examples takes on a third application.

It will help you keep atop payments to the contractor. This is accomplished with another set of modifictions. At **J. Kenneth Fraser and Associates**, the engineers edit columns to reflect current project costs per job. Then, they update columns for quantities per job to reflect past, current, and total estimates. Their spreadsheet automatically tallies the dollar amount and takes into account other factors. Such factors might include: percent of money retained per month, previous payments and money withheld for corrective action for unacceptable wrongs.

In most projects, a "schedule of values" is required from the successful contractor shortly after the contract is signed and sealed. In such a case, the "applications for payment" should be coordinated with the schedule of values and the same procedure following with spreadsheet.

CITY OF FAIRVIEW, FAIRVIEW COUNTY, NEW YORK
CONTRACT NO. 2 - MISC. STREET IMPROVEMENTS

J. KENNETH FRASER & ASSOCIATES, P.C.
CONSULTING ENGINEERS
22 HIGH STREET
RENSSELAER, NEW YORK 12144

ACME CONSTRUCTION, INC.
107 MAIN STREET
FAIRVIEW, NEW YORK 10101

ITEM NO.	DESCRIPTION	PREV EST	THIS EST	TOTAL	UNIT	UNIT $	AMOUNT
01562	DUST CONTROL - CALCIUM CHLORIDE	0.00	0.00	0.00	TON	100.00	0.00
02111.03	TREE REMOVAL (25"-36")	0.00	0.00	0.00	EACH	250.00	0.00
02111.06	STUMP REMOVAL (25"-36")	1.00	0.00	1.00	EACH	100.00	100.00
02200.01	EXCAVATION	2030.10	242.50	2272.60	C.Y.	8.50	19317.10
02200.02	GRANULAR BEDDING	20.00	0.00	20.00	C.Y.	20.00	400.00
02200.03	SELECT FILL	20.00	0.00	20.00	C.Y.	20.00	400.00
02200.04	RUN OF BANK GRAVEL	37.60	0.00	37.60	C.Y.	20.00	752.00
* 02222	ROCK EXCAVATION (1)	0.00	0.00	0.00	C.Y.	30.00	0.00
02272.01	ROAD STABILIZATION FABRIC	4477.20	0.00	4477.20	S.Y.	1.50	6715.80
02510.01	CONCRETE SIDEWALKS & DRIVEWAYS	68.40	12.60	81.00	S.Y.	36.00	2916.00
* 02510.02	ADDITIONAL FIRST CLASS CONCRETE	2.70	0.00	2.70	C.Y.	300.00	810.00
02511	GRAVEL SUB-BASE	1561.90	0.00	1561.90	C.Y.	10.00	15619.00
02513.01	ASPHALT CONCRETE - TYPE 5 SHIM COURSE	500.00	0.00	500.00	TON	50.00	25000.00
02513.05	NEW BITUM. SDWLKS, & DRVWYS - 2-1/2" THICK	0.00	139.00	139.00	S.Y.	15.00	2085.00
02513.06	NEW BITUM. ROADWAYS - 3-1/2" THICK	1989.60	2954.80	4944.40	S.Y.	7.50	37083.00
02513.07	BITUM. PAVEMENT OVERLAY 1"-1-1/2" THICK	0.00	15485.40	15485.40	S.Y.	3.50	54198.90
02528	RE-SET EXISTING STONE CURB	466.70	0.00	466.70	L.F.	10.00	4667.00
02529	PRECAST CONCRETE CURB	1420.20	0.00	1420.20	L.F.	16.00	22723.20
02575.01	CONDITIONING EXISTING PAVEMENT	0.00	15480.00	15480.00	S.Y.	0.65	10062.00

SUBTOTAL $202,849.00

101 Uses For Your A/E Microcomputer

The word database is computer jargon for a familiar and essential item in everyday life. A database is a collection of text and numbers organized and presented to serve specific purposes.

One of the more familiar examples is the telephone directory. This printed database contains the names, addresses and telephone numbers of individuals, businesses and government agencies. The addresses and telephone numbers have little value by themselves. They are useful only when they are related to a name. Other databases include stock reports, dictionaries, accounts receivable ledgers and personnel files.

What distinguishes databases from a newspaper or non-fiction book? The reason is quite specific. In a database, information is presented in a manner that makes it easy to locate a particular piece. In a telephone directory, for example, numbers and addresses are related to the name.

The names are presented in alphabetical order so one can find them easily. Find the name and you have found the phone number. The name is the key to using a telephone book. When you call TELEPHONE INFORMATION, you ask for a number based on a name. The operator then enters that name into a computer and asks the machine to sort through hundreds of thousands of names, in many cases, to find one.

The computer used by TELEPHONE INFORMATION is a large mainframe. But the principle is no different for microcomputers. There are dozens of general-purpose database programs for microcomputers.

Most database packages allow you to create a format for your own "records". A record in a telephone book consists of a name, an address and a telephone number. Each of these parts is termed a "fieldname". A collection of fieldnames is a "field structure", a list that provides a framework for a database.

52 Photographic Prizes

Slides are absolutely essential for documentation and presentation. So what if Ansel Adams didn't take them? In both new and successful practices, slides are a valuable resource. They prove their worth for A/E firms whose business turns on its visually impressive designs.

Like other documents, keeping a list of slides is essential. Without a list, you might look endlessly for a slide. Or you might forget the description of the slide. Frank Mascia, an Arizona architect, has a specialized photo file on a database. His file includes fields for slide number, slide location, type, project, project number, project type, photographer's name, data of slide, subject, interest value, quality and general remarks.

Collaborative Design Group of Tucson, Arizona produced this example:

Record 211 of 211
==
SLIDE NUMBER: -
SLIDE LOCATION: -
TYPE: -
PROJECT: -
PROJECT NUMBER: -
PROJECT TYPE: -
PHOTOGRAPHER: -
DATE OF SLIDE: -
SUBJECT: -
VALUE INTREST: -
QUALITY 1-9: -
REMARKS: -

Type entry or use @ or cmds   32K Avail.

File: PHOTO FILE   REVIEW/ADD/CHANGE   Escape: Main Menu

Selection: All records

Record 131 of 211
==
SLIDE NUMBER: 0131
SLIDE LOCATION: BOOK 5, PAGE 6
TYPE: PHOTO 8X10 COLOR
PROJECT: DOBRAS RESIDENCE
PROJECT NUMBER: 8263
PROJECT TYPE: KITCHEN & BATH REMODEL
PHOTOGRAPHER: JAMES BRETT
DATE OF SLIDE: 1983
SUBJECT: KITCHEN CABINETS & COUNTERS
VALUE INTREST: -
QUALITY 1-9: 8
REMARKS: "House Beautiful" Winter 1984

Type entry or use @ or cmds   @-? for Help

53 Making Good On Holidays

From your office address list, you can
generate individual holiday lists.
Using database software, you separate
friends from business acquaintances.
This process allows you to create targeted
mailings.

To gain this control, assign each
address a code. This tells your
microcomputer which address and name
goes in which mailing list. Remember
how diverse our society has become with
its multitude of celebrations. People
celebrate many holidays depending on
their backgrounds from Christmas to
Passover to Ramadan to Chinese New
Year's.

Todd Lee/FR Clark Associates of Boston,
Massachusetts gave this example:

#	Mssrs	First Name	Last Name	Street	Address	Zip	Fr	Cl
69	Mr.	Stanley	Abercrombie, AIA	475 Park Ave So., 4th Fl.	New York, NY	10016	01	
63	Mr.	Theodore	Amenta	55 High Street	West Hartford, CT	06091	03	21
85	Mr.	Jonathan	Barnett, Director	138th and Convent Avenue	New York, NY	10031	01	31
84	Mr.	Edward F.	Barry, Jr.	286 Congress Street	Boston, MA	02210	03	21
95	Mr.	Kent	Barwick	457 Madison Avenue	New York, NY	10022		
72		Donald	Connors, Esq.	53 State Street	Boston, MA	02109	03	29
89	Mrs.	Joan	Davidson	330 Madison Ave.	New York, NY	10017	01	
55	Mr.	John	DeMonchaux	77 Massachusetts Avenue	Cambridge, MA	02139	02	27
110	Mr.	Peter	Forbes	124 Myrtle Street	Boston, MA	02114	02	
242		Norman	Laliberte	51 Cliffe Street	Nahant, MA	01908	03	
78	Mr.	Albert	Lamb, III, ASLA	711 Boylston Street	Boston, MA	02116	01	02
239	Mr. & Mrs.	Sheridan	Lord	Parsonage Lane	Sagaponack, Long Island,		01	50
183	Ms.	Marianne	MacDonald	129 Commonwealth Avenue	Boston, MA	02116	01	24
185	Mr.	Joseph	Massik	87 Revere Street	Boston, MA	02114	01	28
258	Mr. & Mrs.	James	Mitchell	Sakonnet Vineyards	Little Compton, RI			
34	Mr.	John R.	Myer	14 Arrow Street	Cambridge, MA	02138	01	20
181	Mr.	Barton	Myers	19 Berryman	Toronto, Canada		01	20
233	Mr.	C. McKim	Norton	1040 6th Avenue	New York, NY	10022	01	24
262	Mr.	Timothy J.	O'Toole	480 Commonwealth Avenue	Boston, MA	02215	13	76
170	Mr. & Mrs.	Roswell B.	Perkins	1120 Fifth Avenue	New York, NY	10028	01	
272	Mr.	G.W. Terry	Rankine	1050 Mass. Avenue	Cambridge, MA	02138	01	20
271	Ms.	Sidney	Rockefeller	41 Beacon Street	Boston, MA	02108	28	29
126	Mr. & Mrs.	Benno	Schmidt, Jr.	168 East 95th Street	New York, NY	10028	01	
201	Mr.	Alvin	Schragis	600 Madison Avenue	New York, NY	10022	25	20

54 History On-Line

A/E marketing requires extensive
recordkeeping. Many firms keep project
completion, square-foot costs, and gross
to net profits in a word processing file.
Accessing and analyzing this information
is difficult because word processing does
not sort and index. Since marketing is
really a targeting game, it is better to
use a database, which does have these
capabilities.

Review the type of information you are
currently keeping on projects, and
re-evaluate whether you'd like to improve
that information. If it contains a lot of
data that requires you to scroll
endlessly, then a database is the best
program. It will quickly assemble
information for project proposals and also
give you a sense of your firm's past
record.

Start the database at the beginning of
every project. Keep information at every
stage. This practice will provide a
valuable resource of current information
on every structure your firm is working
on. Moreover, when you are finished with
the project, you will have information on
marketing cost, fee negotiations,
specifications, cost analysis,
prototypical solutions, scheduling and
cost control.

55 Do It Like Interpol

Develop Sherlock Holmes' sixth sense for
finding partners on out-of-state joint
ventures. How? With a database, that's
how. So when a major project bid is
out-of-state, you have the best partner
for the project. Say, for example, there
is a prison re-construction in Wyoming,
and you are an A/E in Kansas who wants to
bid immediately. Turn to your "Slammer
Planners" database file and look for a
firm that has built prisons in Wyoming or
surrounding states.

You should keep a history of the firms'
work with comments about its
qualifications. You build the database by
attending conferences, conventions,
clipping trade magazines and architectural
publications. Remember that "database
maintenance" requires time. So spend time
working on your database. It will more
than return its value in terms of time
saved when that prison project appears
over the horizon.

56 Managing Your Reading

Every good A/E firm's library consists of books, periodicals and documents. And what else? This one item makes all the difference in the world. It is the difference between having a library and having a collection of disparate books. Can't guess?

It's what makes the Library of Congress the nation's central library. Without it, the Library of Congress would be nothing more than a trash heap.

A catalog, of course.

Do you have one for your firm's library? If you don't -- and even if do -- you should consider using a database for cataloguing. Whenever new material arrives, it is carefully labeled using one the Library of Congress system (Dewey Decimal has taken a backseat). Then, someone (find someone who loves detail work) is assigned to spend a day, a month entering title, author, and catalog numbers.

J. Kenneth Fraser & Associates of Rensselaer, New York provides an example:

LIBRARY FILE TO DATE

TITLE	CATALOG
=====	=======
ASSESSMENT OF HYDROPOWER RESTORATION & EXPANSION IN NYS	TC 146 N19
BLENHEIM-GILBOA PUMPED-STORAGE PROJECT - POWER AUTHORITY NY	TC·146 M15
CHOICE OF HYDRO-ELECTRIC EQUIPMENT FOR TIDAL ENERGY	TC 150 K70
DUXBURY DEMONSTRATION PROJECT - SMALL HYDROELECTRIC SYSTEM	TC 140 T65
FEASIBILITY STUDIES FOR SMALL SCALE HYDROPOWER ADDITIONS	TC 147 U72
HARNESSING WATER POWER FOR HOME ENERGY	TK 1081 M26
HYDRO PLANT CONSTRUCTION - COST & ANNUAL PRODUCTION	TK 1191 U75
HYDRO TURBINES	TC 147
HYDROELECTRIC GENERATION ON PARK-ORIENTED RIVERS	TK 2896 N31
HYDROELECTRIC POWER - VOLUME 1 - HYDRAULIC DEVELOPMENT & EQUIP.	TC 147 L90
HYDROELECTRIC POWER EVALUATION	TK 1191 U74
HYDROELECTRIC POWER PROJECTS LICENSED BY FED. POWER COMMISSION	TC 145 F50
HYDROELECTRIC POWER RESOURCES OF THE UNITED STATES	TC 145 F48
HYDROPOWER - AN ENERGY SOURCE WHOSE TIME HAS COME AGAIN	TC 147 C85
HYDROPOWER COST ESTIMATING MANUAL	TC 147 U73
HYDROPOWER UTILIZATION IN NEW YORK STATE - NYSERDA	TC 147 P67
ISSUES RELATED TO SMALL SCALE HYDRO - INSTREAM FLOW NEEDS	TC 140 O22
LOWER LIMITS - LOW-HEAD HYDROELECTRIC INSTALLATIONS	TK 1191 T95
NYS BARGE CANAL SYSTEM EVALUATION OF HYDROPOWER POTENTIAL	TC 147 P70
NYS SMALL HYDROPOWER DEVELOPMENT PROGRAM - A STATUS REPORT	TC 146 N16
NYSERDA - HYDROPOWER ASSESSMENT OF THE NYS BARGE CANAL	TC 147 P65
POTENTIAL FOR HYDROPOWER DEVELOPMENT/EXIST. DAMS NEW ENGLAND	TC 147 N25
PROBLEMS OF HYDROELECTRIC DEVELOPMENT AT EXISTING DAMS	TC 147 B30
RECONNAISSANCE STUDY OF SELECTED HYDROELECTRIC SITES	TC 148 F81
SITE OWNER'S MANUAL FOR SMALL SCALE HYDROPOWER DEVELOPMENT	TC 147 P69

57 Product Literature Filing

Product information comes through the mail every day. Though it often has negligible initial value, it soon becomes a valuable collective resource. Successful cross-referencing and indexing puts it into a neat, accessible package for every member of your firm.

Such tasks befit databases. They allow you to keep track of pounds of manufacturer's glossy brochures and serious looking spec sheets. **J. Kenneth Fraser and Associates** of Rensselaer, New York has developed an extensive database index of product information based on Construction Specification Institute numbers. They created the following structure: manufacturer, product, CSI numbers, sub-catagory number and date of arrival. These fields allow information searches based on manufacturer's name and product.

Fraser offers the accompanying example:

PRODUCTS (CSI) INDEX -- DATABASE PRINTOUT

MANUFACTURER	PRODUCT	CSI NO.	SUBCAT NO	DATE
ARMCO	MULTI-PLATE BOX CULVERT	02720	AR	SEPTEMBER 1981
ARMCO INC.	METAL BUILDING SYSTEMS	13122	AR	AUGUST 1979
ARMCO INC.	METAL BUILDING SYSTEMS	13122	AR	AUGUST 1979
ARMCO STEEL CORPORATION	MULTI-PLATE SUPER-SPAN	05010	AR	JULY 1973
ARMCO STEEL CORPORATION	BUILDING SYSTEMS	13120	AR	JUNE 1977
ARMCO, INC.	REINFORCED PLASTIC MANHOLES	02605	AR	NOVEMBER 1978
ARMCO, INC.	SPECIAL ANALYSIS STEEL PIPE	02610	AR	OCTOBER 1977
ARMCO, INC.	ALUMINIZED STEEL PIPE PIPE-ARCH	02610	AR	NOVEMBER 1979
ARMCO, INC.	FIBERGLASS SEWER MANHOLES	02605	AR	NONE LISTED
ARMCO, INC.	EPOXY-BONDED PIPE & PIPE ARCH	02610	AR	FEBRUARY 1979
ARMCO, INC.	DESIGN MANUAL FOR TRUSS PIPE	02610	AR	JUNE, 1969
ARMCO CONSTRUCTION PRODUCTS	CORRUGATED STEEL PIPE	02610	AR	RECEIVED 1984
ARMCO BUILDING SYSTEMS	METAL BUILDING SYSTEMS	13122	AR*	1979
ARMCO STEEL CORPORATION	GATES - IRRIGATION & LOW HEAD APPL.	11285	AR	MARCH 1975
ARMCO CONSTRUCTION PRODUCTS	GRAVITY SANITARY SEWER PIPE	02610	AR	RECEIVED 1984
ARMCO STEEL PRODUCTS	SEWER PIPE	02610	AR*	RECEIVED 1971
ARMCO CONSTRUCTION PRODUCTS	PIPE, BRIDGE PLANK, RETAINING WALLS	15050	AR*	RECEIVED 1977

58 Know The Suppliers

Suppose you have a report to write and the
KROY machine is out of tape. Worse yet!
The plan-desk personnel is out sick.
There is an easy, safe solution to ensure
that supplies are around or at least
available. Keep an address list of
suppliers in a database in the drafting
room, marketing department or plan desk.
You will save yourself a lot of time if
you have it updated and printed out
regularly. It sure beats keeping around a
Rolodex, which demands daily attention
from your secretary.

59 Optimize Finish Schedule

The elements of a room are endless:
floorbases, wainscots, walls, windows,
rugs, lighting and sashes. A/E's hold the
magical wand that decides height of a
ceiling, square footage and color, among
other specifications. Out of this bevy of
inches, reds, vinyl and fluorescent comes
the finish and materials schedule --
working drawings and cost estimate
information.

Managing this information requires
superior coordination, hours of office
support and a talent for detail. If you
don't have all, or three, or even one, you
do now. Create the schedule in a database
and, like all your other lists, update and
massage it whenever necessary. Use the
schedule for recording design decisions in
your bid proposal, to coordinate
consultants work, for a punch list and for
facilities management.

Rolland Thompson supplied this example:

WEST CONCORD UNION CHURCH

MATERIALS and FINISH SCHEDULE

** FLOOR 0

RM NO	ROOM NAME	FLOORING	CARPET	BASE	WALLS	CLG	HGT	AREA	REMARKS
001	LOWER VESTIBULE	conc	$20/SY	WD NAT	BLEO PL	ACT	9.00	0.00	Level conc slab to receive carpet, hang clg lay-in tile, blue bd wall+skim coat pnt, millwork = [base, chair rail, clg moulding, trimmed openings/arches], incandescent lights, new radiation.
001.A	CLOSET	conc		yes	WD PNT	GMB PNT	GMB PNT	10.00	0.00	Assign to committee or user: [Millwork: shelving above, cabinets below]
001.B	Closet	VYL		yes	WD PNT	GMB	GMB	9.00	0.00	Assign to user or committee
001.C	STORAGE RM # 1	CONC/HARD	-	-	CMU PNT	GMB ?	10.00	0.00	[HVAC: louvered door for ventilation,], [ELEC: fluorescent]
001.D	STORAGE ROOM #2	VYL	-	PLAM	PLAM	LVR	7.50	0.00	[HVAC: louvered door for ventialtion], [ELEC: flusorescent] Millwork: 1 3/8" door and lock
002	CORRIDOR	conc	20$/SY	WD NAT	BLEO PNT	ACT	9.00	0.00	Same treatment as lower vestibule, space 001.
002.A	CLEANING CL.. A	conc		-	WD PNT	GMB PNT	GMB PNT	10.00	0.00	Millwork:(4-18" adjustable shelving @ side, perforated BD in rear for hanging equipment/tools, 1 3/8" hollow core door, hardware + lock)
002.B	CLEANING CLOSET	conc		-	GMB	GMB PNT	10.00	0.00	Assigned to general use, [Millwork: storage shelving and Perforated hardboard, light, conv. outlet, 1 3/8" hollow core, hardware + lock.)
002.C	ELECTRIC CLOSET	CNC		-	WD PNT	CNC BLK	GMB PNT	10.00	0.00	For incoming electric service, main distribution panel, meter, etc.
005	CRAWL SPACE	conc		-	conc	conc	9.98	37.70	[HVAC: remove unused piping, insulate domestic hot water]
006.	STORAGE RM # 3	concr pnt	-	9" wd PNT	pl PNT	pl PNT	9.98	61.60	Remove vestibule door, close opening with wd studs, gwb/blbd and pl on vestibule side, double glaze window[HVAC: insulate steam + domestic]
007	CLASS ROOM # 1	VAT	grey	8" wd PNT	plp PNT	plp PNT	10.00	1015.30	Specialty:add track mounted bulletin boards on west wall for separate use by Montessori and Church Schools [HVAC:insulate steam [ELEC:new fixtures]

60 Customize Your Schedule

With a well organized and properly coded materials and finish schedule, it is possible to create specialized schedules. You could code your database for closets and storage rooms. The database will then extract information and put it into your specified format.

The accompanying example is from redesign efforts at the West Concord Union Church in Concord, Massachusetts. It provides a summary of storage space. It includes room numbers, closet numbers and location, area, width, user assignment and general remarks.

Once you have filled your database you are in a position to quantify space. Also, if your remarks are kept current, you will know the details about louvers, locks, shelf space and users' habits.

SUMMARY OF CLOSETS & STORAGE ROOMS
Assignments

RM NO	CLOSET	AREA	WIDTH	ASSIGNMENT	REMARKS
** 0					
001.A	CLOSET	7.9	4.5		Assign to committee or user: [Millwork: shelving above, cabinets below]
001.B	Closet	6.6	3.8		Assign to user or commitee
001.C	STORAGE RM # 1	24.0	8.0		[HVAC: louvered door for ventilation,], [ELEC: fluorescent]
001.D	STORAGE ROOM #2	24.0	8.0		Install hydaulic elevator with two side doors (N & W), three stops, basement, vestibule, and 1st floor, [ELEC:machine power, fluorescent;telephone]
002.A	SUPPLY CL. A	13.5	4.5	Building	Millwork=(4-18" adjustable shelving @ side, perforated BD in rear for hanging equipment/tools, 1 3/8" hollow core door, hardware + lock)
002.B	CLEANING CLOSET	21.0	7.0	Building	Assigned to general use,[Millwork: storage shelving and Perforated hardboard, light, conv. outlet,1 3/8" hollow core, hardware + lock)
002.C	ELECTRIC CLOSET	13.5	4.5		For incoming electric service, main distribution panel, meter, etc.
006.	STORAGE RM # 3	61.6	0.0		Remove vestibule door, close opening with wd studs, gwb/blbd and pl on vestibule side, double glaze window[HVAC: insulate steam + domestic]
007.A	CHRISTIAN ED	35.0	10.0	Christian Ed	Millwork = (install Bifold doors, 2-18" high shelves), keep floor clear for caster-mounted furniture, [ELEC: fluorescent]
007.B	STORAGE	8.3	4.8	Montessori	Assign to Montessori
009.	STORAGE RM # 4	80.7	0.0		No change
010.A	CLOSET	6.0	4.0	Council	One of 2 closets installed for: Senior High + unamed Church Committee. Millwork = (4-15" deep adjustable shelves)
010.B	closet	6.0	4.0	Trustees	Assign to user [15" shelving]
011.A	MAINTENANCE CL.	45.3	10.0	Building Maint	CMU to form storage closet with metal door, louver, millwork =(two sets of 18" deep wood shelves, 5 each side + tool hanging strips), check interference with fresh air, HVAC controls
012.A	CLOSET	9.0	4.5		Assign to church committee or outside user. millwork =(1 3/8" door, 4-15" deep adjustable wd shelves, hardware + lock)
012.B	CLOSET	9.0	4.5		"
012.C	CLOSET	9.0	4.5		"
012.D	CLOSET	6.9	2.5		"
016.A	CLOSET	10.5	5.2	Concord Guild	Assign to user
016.B	CLOSET	10.5	5.2	Concord Guild	Assign to user
016.C	CLOSET	5.0	2.0	Grange	Assign to user
017.	STORAGE RM # 3	62.1	0.0		Rehabilitate and modify sanctuary heater, insulate West opening. Assign to Archives, install safe
018.A	CLOSET	10.1	4.5		Assign to committee or user
018.B	CLOSET	10.1	4.5		Assign to committee or user
019.	STORAGE RM # 6	0.0	0.0		Assigned to dining table storage on moveable racks

61 Tracking Drawings

Design professionals possess the skills
and experience to solve all the issues of
construction. But how do they use these
skills? They don't really make
"blueprints". They simply manage
numerical, graphic, and textual
information. Managing that information is
greatly facilitated by a database.

Drawing lists are a good example. It is
hard enough to get a designer to put a
date on a drawing, let alone make a list
from it. So set up a database for
drawings -- project by project. Include
in your database the following:
prototypical spaces by drawing number,
pre-schematics and zoning/feasibility
studies, site and environmental reports,
schematics, bid documents and construction
documents.

Develop a numbering system that keeps
track of your projects chronologically. A
common technique is a five-digit number
like 8514A. Take 8514A. This records the
first item for addition on the fourteenth
project in the year 1985.

62 Reduce Overlay Confusion

If you are a convert to overlay drafting, then you probably know the confusion it brings to the design process. How do you keep track of which drawing becomes part of the overlay and which one doesn't, which sheet requires the grid and which base becomes screened?

Here's another use for that original drawing file. Use it for an overlay drafting checklist. Delete nonessential information.

Turn it into a document that accounts for the overlays. You will realize substantial time savings. And, when you add a consultant's work to your overlay collection, you don't have to guess anymore about its place.

Rolland Thompson offers this example:

TODD LEE/F R CLARK Associates, Inc.   Project Name: SIDEWALK NO. 1
148 State Street   Project Nos.: 8627, 8627.A thru G
Boston, MA 02109   Date: June 23, 1986

Drawing Size: 24" x 36" — 6.0 SF

DRAWING #	DESCRIPTION	Scale	I SCHEM 50%	I SCHEM 100%	II DD 50%	II DD 100%	III CONTRACT 40%	III CONTRACT 75%	III CONTRACT 100%	IV BID ADD.	V CONSTRUC	COMMENTS (O = "Overlay")
	SITEWORK											
L-200	Contours	1:240				*		*	*			O
L-201	Paving	1:240	*	*		*	*	*	*			O
L-202	Planting	1:240				*		*	*			O
	CIVIL											
C-200	Civil, Grades	1:240						*	*			O
C-201	Utilities	1:240				*	*	*	*			O
C-202	Site Lighting	1:240			*	*	*	*	*			O
	STRUCTURAL											
S-200	Foundation	1/8		*	*	*	*	*	*			O
S-201	1st Floor	1/8		*	*	*	*	*	*			O
S-202	2nd Floor	1/8		*		*	*	*	*			O
S-203/6	3rd-6th Floors	1/8		*		*	*	*	*			O
S-207	Roof	1/8				*	*	*	*			O
S-208	Schedules/Dtls	3/4				*	*	*	*			
S-209	Detail	3/4						*	*			
	ARCHITECTURAL											
A-200	Basement	1/8		*	*	*	*	*	*			O
A-201	1st Floor	1/8	*	*	*	*	*	*	*			O
A-202	2nd Floor	1/8	*	*	*	*	*	*	*			O
A-203/6	3rd-6th Floor	1/8	*	*	*	*	*	*	*			O
A-207	Roof	1/8		*		*		*	*			O
A-208	Lobby/Toilets	1/4			*	*	*	*	*			O
	REFLECTED CLG											
A-201R	RF 1st Floor	1/8		*	*	*	*	*	*			O
A-202R	RF 2nd Floor	1/8			*	*	*	*	*			O
A-203/6R	RF 3rd-6th Fl	1/8		*	*	*	*	*	*			O
	ELEVATIONS											
A-301	N/S Elevations	1/8	*	*		*		*	*			O
A-302	E/W Elevations	1/8	*	*		*		*	*			O
A-303	AA/BB Sections	1/8		*		*		*	*			O
	EXTERIOR DTLS											
A-401	Wall Sections	3/4	*	*		*	*	*	*			
A-402	Entrances	3/4		*		*	*	*	*			
A-403	Details	AN					*	*	*			
A-404	Roof Dtls, Misc	3/4						*	*			
	INTERIOR DTLS											
A-501	Parts./Doors	3/4		*		*		*	*			
A-502	Details	1 1/2				*		*	*			
A-503	Details	AN							*			
	CIRCULATION											
A-601	Stairs	1/4						*	*			
A-602	Elevs./Exter.	AN				*		*	*			
	MECHANICAL											
M-200	Basement	1/8		*								O
M-201	1st Floor	1/8	*	*	*	*	*	*	*			O
M-202	2nd Floor	1/8		*		*	*	*	*			O
M-203/6	3rd-6th Floors	1/8		*		*		*	*			O
M-207	Roof	1/8				*			*			O
M-208	Schedules	AN				*	*	*	*			
	CONTINUED											

63 Finishes Listing

The punchlist is the bane of the design
profession. Most specifications require
everyone connected with a project to
punchlist their activities. In theory, it
is the contractor's responsibility. In
practice, the client pressures the
architect or engineer to handle the
detailed chore of annotating every
incomplete or incorrect item.

Do your punchlist on a database. It makes
it much easier to list items and then to
update your punchlist at completion.
Treat your list like a list of machine
codes. This is a much easier technique
than word processing since you aren't
required to alter the main file -- just
respond to prompts.

64 Electrical Approvals

Consider making a separate database for electrical work from your architectural finishes database. This means you tailor the list for the project at hand with new codes for outlets and switches, fixtures and lighting, speakers, audio-visual and panel boards.

65 Se Defendendo

Lawyers are not a popular sight at a job site. To keep them away and yet involved with a project, provide as much documentation as possible on problems at the job site. Keeping your lawyer current on your activities will help save face in court. For example, a developer might forget he failed to ask you to fast-track a project and to go into construction with incomplete "scope" drawings. When change orders come pouring in, the hackles rise and suing becomes the order of the day.

Let your database paper your activities . Set fields for every necessary record. Set up a field called "Action:By" and another called "When". In the first one, you can fill in a name or a code to indicate who is responsible for following up on a meeting decision. Use a five-digit letter code for the finish date. Generate an action report by listing demands on the owner, the architect, the consulting engineer, the construction manager. If you should ever go to court, you have evidence you have exercised "reasonable care" and are not negligent.

Dr. Robert M. Dryden
601 N. Wilmot, Suite 58
Tucson, Arizona 85711

PROJECT: DRYDEN MEDICAL

PROJECT NUMBER: 8526

PROJECT MEMO

The Following Constitutes My Understanding Of The Items
Discussed And The Conclusions Reached. If There Are Any
Additions Or Corrections, Please Contact The Undersigned.

PHASE COMPLETION: 11:11:85

As per our agreement I am requesting authorization to begin the next
    phase of the basic architectural services for your new offices.
    The Schematic Design Services are complete.

Completed Schematic Design Service Summary:
1. Review and evaluation of owner's program for requirements .
2. Review of owner's program with private and government health
    facility consultants.
        A. Pat Vega
        B. State Health Department
        C. Benson Optical
        D. City of Tucson, Building Safety Department
        E. City of Tucson, Planning and Zoning
3. Review with owner, of several alternative approaches for the design
    of the project.
4. Preparation of several sets of drawings and sketches. Drawings
    delivered to you at our meeting on October 23, 1985 constitute the
    final schematic phase drawings.
5. Submittal of a Statement of Probable Construction cost based on
    current area and volume indicated on the October 23, drawings.
    Updated drawings indicating a minor change to the Outpatient
    Surgery entry were also deliverd to your office on October
    28,1985.

Per your request I am required to obtain your written approval to
    begin each architectural service phase for your project. After
    your review of the drawings and Probable Cost Statement, your
    signature on a copy of this memo will serve as acceptance of the
    Schematic Design and the authorization to begin Design
    Development.

Frank Mascia, Architect

Approved: _____   Date:_____

          Robert M. Dryden, M.D.

COLLABORATIVE DESIGN GROUP 2555 E. FIRST ST. TUCSON ARIZONA 85716

---

101 Uses For Your A/E Microcomputer

66   The Bad Apple

Scattered about every office is a list of
contractors, subcontractors, suppliers,
and manufacturers you and your associates
have had experience with. You owe it to
your client and your own peace of mind to
keep track of subs and their performance
on projects. Rather than foraging through
files, racking your brain, or starting
from scratch with the yellow pages, set up
a database that includes specific data
useful in lining up suppliers for the
next project.

Use the database sorting capabilities to
keep yourself aware of who is blacklisted
and blackballed. Now you are developing a
discrete technique to record bad
performance that you don't want to live
with again.

NYC has blacklisted certain paint
contractors only to have them reappear
bidding for city projects under a new
name. For example, the new company might
have the name of a girl friend's pet dog,
"Deathgrip Painting Company, Inc.". A
computerized database will allow you to
keep up with names behind the aliases.

67 Don't Wait For Contractors

Contractors are notoriously slow to hand over shop drawing schedules. It's extremely frustrating to ask for them repeatedly. Contractors usually wait until their sub-contractors generate lists. They like to call it delegation.

This practice delays the delivery of the list to the A/E's, who will hold up payment to the contractors. Such a situation just throws salt into a wound in the relationship between the contractor and the A/E's.

Here's a means to prevent this situation. Don't wait for the contractor. Turn project specifications into shop drawings on your word processor. You could also flag product data and samples requested from the contractor. When you are done with the shop drawing schedule, throw in a disclaimer that the list is not all encompassing and requires the contractor to add dates. Contractors are quick to acquiesce.

CSI number	author (trade)	drawing number	drawing title	s t	c t	s #	schedule date	receipt date	to cnslt date	fr cnslt date	return date	a
03300-001	BOSTON SAND		LETTER 400 PSI CONE	D	S	1	/ /	01/03/83	01/04/83	01/19/83	01/24/83	
05100-001	ANTONELLI IRONWORKS	E1	STRUCTURAL STEEL	D	S	1	/ /	12/03/82	12/06/82	12/15/82	12/15/82	R
05100-001	ANTONELLI IRONWORKS	E1	STRUCTURAL STEEL	D	S	2	/ /	01/04/83	01/06/83	01/06/83	01/07/83	R
05100-001	ANTONELLI IRONWORKS	E1	STRUCTURAL STEEL	D	S	3	/ /	01/24/83	/ /	/ /	/ /	
05100-002	ANTONELLI IRONWORKS	E2	STRUCTURAL STEEL	D	S	1	/ /	12/03/82	12/06/82	12/15/82	12/15/82	R
05100-002	ANTONELLI IRONWORKS	E2	STRUCTUR^L STEEL	D	S	2	/ /	01/04/83	01/04/83	01/06/83	01/07/83	R
05100-002	ANTONELLI IRONWORKS	E2	STRUCTURAL STEEL	D	S	3	/ /	01/24/83	/ /	/ /	/ /	
05100-002	ANTONELLI IRONWORKS	E2	STRUCTURAL STEEL	D	S	4	/ /	/ /	/ /	/ /	/ /	
05100-003	ANTONELLI IRONWORKS	E3	STRUCTURAL STEEL	D	S	1	/ /	01/05/83	01/05/83	/ /	/ /	
08410-001	KARAS AND KARAS	1 of 12	MAIN FLOOR PLAN	D	A	1	/ /	12/15/82	/ /	/ /	/ /	
15300-002	LAPPIN BROTHERS		CHILLER PHYSICAL DATA	D	O	1	/ /	01/07/83	01/07/83	/ /	/ /	
15300-002	LAPPIN BROTHERS		CHILLER PHYSICAL DATA	D	O	2	/ /	01/07/83	01/07/83	01/24/83	01/24/83	A
16920-001	NAGER ELECTRIC	no. 5	MOTOR CONTROLS	D	E	1	/ /	01/23/83	/ /	/ /	/ /	

JOB00001:   WARNINGS   (Author,15)

Date: 01/24/83

return in two days

CSI number	author (trade)	drawing number	drawing title	s t	c t	s #	schedule date	receipt date	to cnslt date	fr cnslt date	return date	a
05100-003	ANTONELLI IRONWORKS	E3	STRUCTURAL STEEL	D	S	1	/ /	01/05/83	01/05/83	/ /	/ /	

return today

CSI number	author (trade)	drawing number	drawing title	s t	c t	s #	schedule date	receipt date	to cnslt date	fr cnslt date	return date	a
03300-001	BOSTON SAND		LETTER 400 PSI CONE	D	S	1	/ /	01/03/83	01/04/83	01/19/83	/ /	

late return

CSI number	author (trade)	drawing number	drawing title	s t	c t	s #	schedule date	receipt date	to cnslt date	fr cnslt date	return date	a
08410-001	KARAS AND KARAS	1 of 12	MAIN FLOOR PLAN	D	A	1	/ /	12/15/82	/ /	/ /	/ /	

Computer-Aided Design

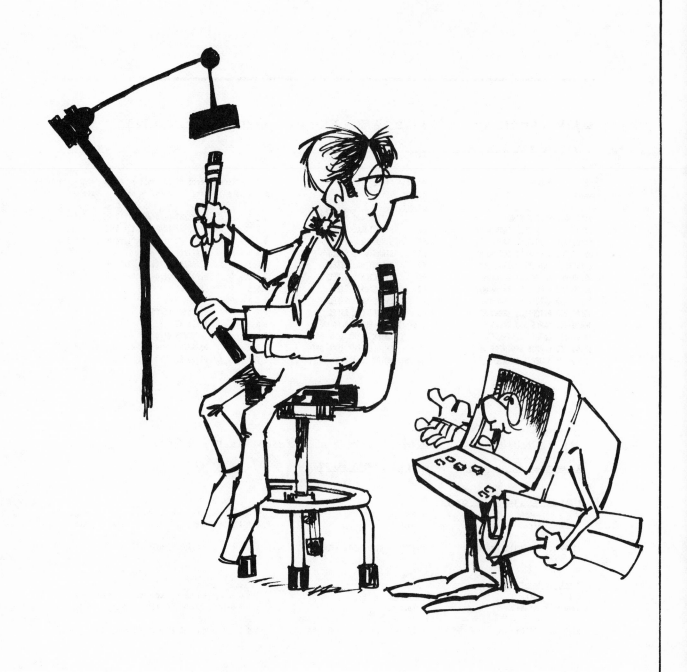

Micro-based computer-aided design systems -- "microCAD" -- offer the ability to create, cut and paste, edit and revise A/E drawings electronically. They also store and retrieve professional drawings, just like the larger, more expensive turnkey systems.

The original two-dimensional systems were developed for mechanical, printed-circuit and architectural designing. Today, the definition of microCAD has expanded with an increase in applications. Yes, it encompasses business graphics, though that is a simplistic use of graphics. But -- more importantly -- microCAD is a professional drafting tool that creates professional engineering schematics and architectural designs.

When compared to manual drafting, microCAD has several advantages and disadvantages. You must always deal with an electronic image during drawing. Thus, you lose that immediacy of a pencil and yellow trace. MicroCAD compensates for this disadvantage with special features such as built bottom-up symbols.

Another advantage is the capability to electronically record data based on coordinates. Consequently, drawing descriptions have no intrinsic scale or dimension. So when an image is called up on the screen -- or turned into a hardcopy drawing on a plotter -- you assign the scale. This allows you to "zoom" in on an area or to "pan" across the full drawing to rework specific sections. The ability to work at different scales ends the need to generate separate drawings for details.

Since each image consists of symbols of walls or doors they are easily moved and copied. You build structures with them. Because you are capable of storing the symbols, you are in a position to use them endlessly, ending a major headache faced during manual drafting on a larger scale.

Many of the more sophisticated uses of microCAD require special programming. In almost all the uses mentioned in this section, there is no special programming. Where programming is required, it has been noted. The purpose of this section is to illustrate uses that are accomplished with most commercially available software.

68 The Initial Hello

Your firm has great service and a tremendous track record. You may grow meek, however, whenever a major client comes to your office. How do you say hello with a bang?

Computer Controls Corp., which works primarily with **Fortune 10** companies, has a solution. It uses CAD to create its welcome sign. A generic sign is kept on file and customized when a Ford or a General Electric comes by for a meeting. Though not a highly sophisticated touch, it has impressed customers who like to walk away with their personalized poster-size signs in hard copy.

WELCOMES

General Electric

6 9 Memorable Images

Who can forget when newspapers ran photos
of the little girl crying on a road in
Vietnam? It changed many feelings about
the war. Strong visuals speak powerfully.

Isn't it worth it then to have an
attractive logo on all your drawings,
stationary, change orders, envelopes,
transmittals and forms? Though people will
rarely say something about your logo, they
will learn to identify it with your firm.

The image-making machine of the future is
a microcomputer. Use the same CAD system
that you used for drawings of
subdivisions. Turn the system into a
graphic arts tool. Either digitize a
design from a magazine or someone else's
stationary -- and alter it to your liking.
Or be really daring and cleverly sketch
with the lines, arcs and splines.

Computer Controls Corp. of Wilmington,
Massachusetts provided the accompanying
example:

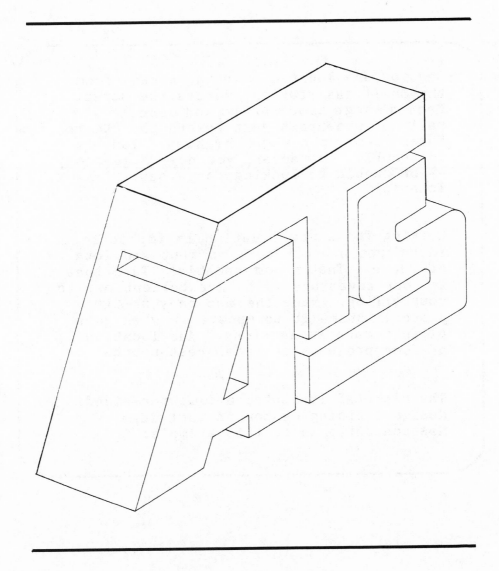

70 The Map Solution

Say you are located down the street from the Shell gas station, across the street from a large supermarket and beneath a railroad underpass just beyond the "Do Not Enter" sign to a major highway. You are in trouble. Moreover, you need a good map -- or should be looking for a better location.

Looking for a new location is impractical. You've got a great deal on rent and lots of space. That's commendable. Turn that to your advantage with an excellent map to your office. Make the map on your CAD system. Store it to update it when your clients make suggestions. Add locations of your projects or local restaurants.

The MicroCAD Insitute, a computer-aided design training center in Cambridge, Massachusetts lends this example:

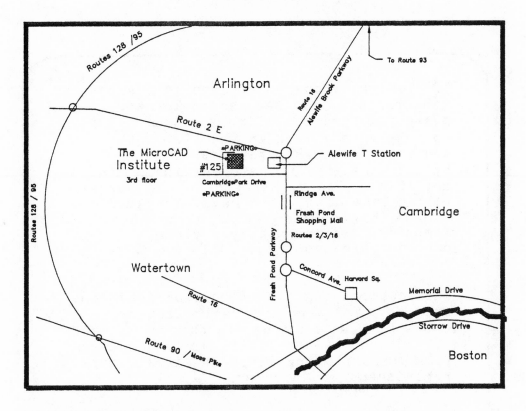

By Public Transportation:
     Take the RED LINE train to the Alewife Station.   Exit onto
     CambridgePark Drive.   #125 is the third building on the
     right.

From Route 128 / 95, West of Boston:
     Take Route 2 East.
     Bear Right at the Traffic Circle at the intersection
     of Route 16 (The Alewife Brook Parkway).
     Take First Right at Traffic Lights, past the MBTA Alewife
     Station.   #125 is the third building on right.
     Parking available behind building or across street.

From Downtown Boston / Storrow Drive / Memorial Drive:
     Take Route 2 West (Fresh Pond Parkway).
     Go past the Fresh Pond Shopping Center and over railroad
     bridge.
     Take next Left, as if you were going into the MBTA Alewife
     Station.   #125 is the third building on right.
     Parking available behind building or across the street.

71 Mercator Missed CAD

If Flemish cartographer Gerhard Kremer
Mercator had used CAD, he could have
generated hundreds of maps a year. But
poor Mercator lived in the sixteenth
century, when cartographers lived or died
by the strength of their drawing
abilities. Today, Mercator would marvel
at the ease with which David Arnold of
D. C. A. Engineering in Henniker, New
Hampshire designs highly stylized
cartographic symbols for his maps.

The accompanying directional arrow is one
example. The arrow, a basic item on
every D. C. A. drawing, is functional and
attractive. Among other nice touches, D.
C. A. uses flowing lines and italic type
reminiscent of Mercator.

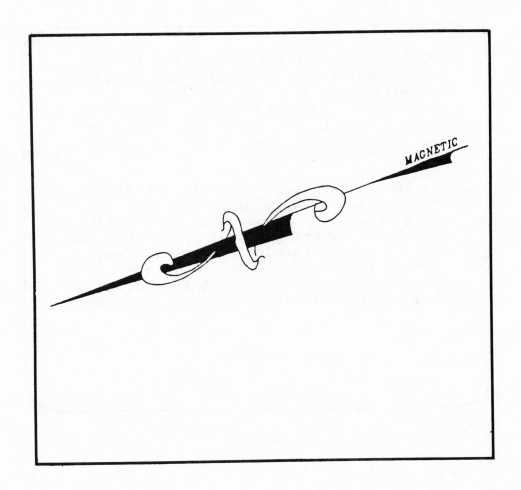

MAGNETIC

72 Play Ad Genius

Why is there such disparity between advertisements in publications? Simple. The publications do the bad ones. Professional designers sensitive to a firm's image do the good ones. This is not true in every case -- but in too many.

Use CAD to gain control over your display advertisments. Write your own copy and design your advertisements. It doesn't have to be anything fancy. Just what you want. **Galson Technical Services, Inc.** does this routinely with employment advertisements. The result is a simple, clean design without embarrassing typos.

73 Books and Rows

Ever wandered into a library looking for a
book? You know how difficult it is walk
to the right shelf immediately.
Instinctively, you look for a librarian or
a map.

It is doubtful that your inhouse library
has a fulltime librarian. If that's the
case, use CAD to create the next best
thing a map of your shelves. On your
map you could include the layout of the
library, label shelves with Library of
Congress numbers, and show seating.

Galson and Galson Consulting Engineers of
East Syracuse, New York supply the
accompanying example:

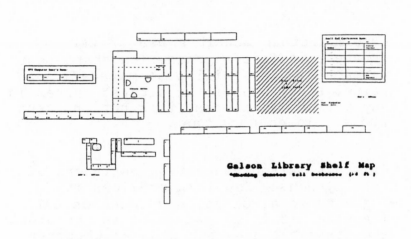

Galaon Library Shelf Map

74 End Power Plays

Who is support staff and what do they do?
Don't fool your subordinates about where
they fit into your A/E firm.

Here's another sensible use of CAD.
Create an office organization chart that
reveals all. It will push management's
value, since one of the biggest gripes in
any office comes when it is not apparent
who should do what task.

Galson & Galson consulting engineers of
East Syracuse, New York provides its
organizational chart, developed on CAD.
The chart is filed away -- after printouts
are distributed -- and altered whenever
staff changes are made.

PROJECT TABLE OF ORGANIZATION

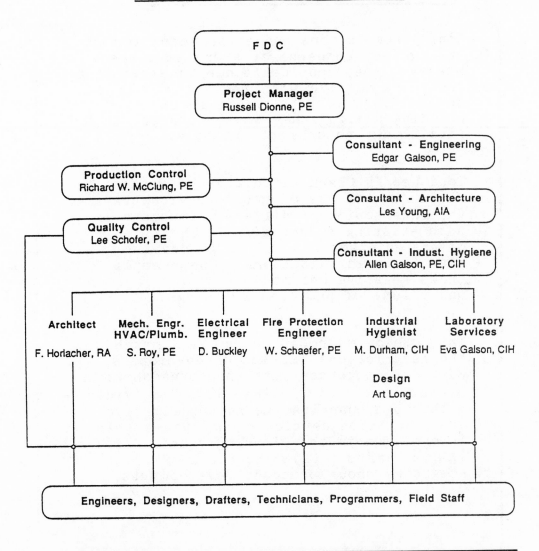

75 3-D Zoning

Zoning regulations and environment impact are two key concerns of every developer. Whenever they consider a new investment, they have to live with those concerns. So when they turn to an A/E about building design, they want a concept that fits sticky government criteria.

Todd Lee/FR Clark Associates of Boston, Massachusetts use microCAD to visualize the interaction of different concepts with existing surroundings. The firm offers an example of microCAD drawing that fulfills this chore. The example shows relative heights and volume of proposed buildings.

This use of microCAD helps A/E's match the restrictions imposed on developers. MicroCAD, together with the spreadsheet in example entitled "Zoning Plays," provides a thorough quantitative and qualitative analysis. The developer then gives this information to the planning board -- and in some cases quells the fears of neighbors about proposed developments.

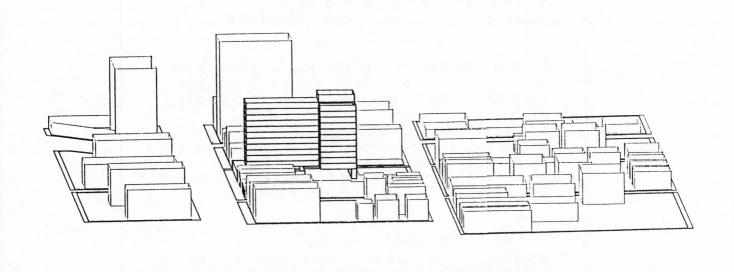

76 Commanding Respect

Who's in charge of what project
responsibilities? Who are the soldiers
working? Sometimes it is difficult to
know. This bit of personnel knowledge
becomes extremely important when a firm
sends its personnel into the field.

Galson and Galson consulting engineers of
East Syracuse, New York had this problem
with its industrial hygiene group. Many
of the group worked in the field
collecting survey information, making it
difficult to keep control of the group's
personnel. But a good use of CAD
prevented chaos and helped clients
understand the chain of command.

The group developed an organization
project table. Among other things, the
table details responsibilities by title,
chain of command, available in-house
consultants and a list of additional
staff available in a time crunch.

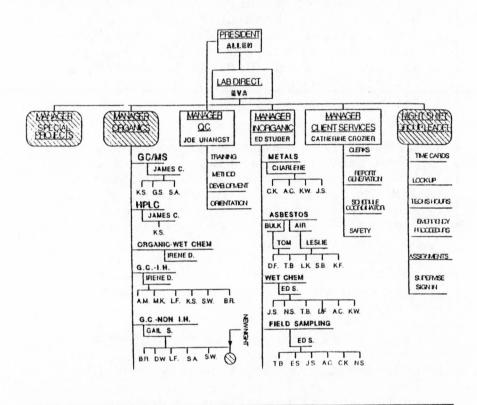

77 Your Own Critical Path

The science of management exploded during World War II. From this horror came "critical path methodology," among other highly innovative management techniques. It gave the U. S. Defense Department an organized means to unify the nation's war effort.

Critical path methodology continues to serve as a planning tool. It has been incorporated into many A/E practices. CPM, as it is known, shows the logical sequence of tasks within a project, indicating when work can proceed in parallel or series -- and at what pace. It allows you to find the critical time, the path where most time is spent and allows you to figure out where to cut corners.

Most A/E firms use some form of CPM. Many have specialized software for their microcomputers that does the work for them. If so, it is possible to use CAD to illustrate the output from that software. If you don't own CPM software, you should improvise with CAD and/or spreadsheets to create a timetable.

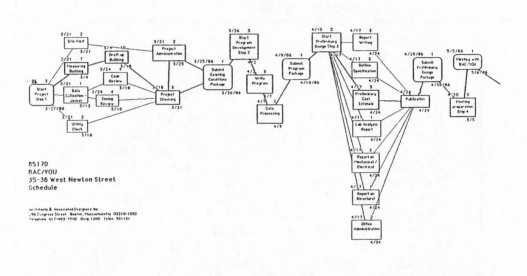

85170
BAC/YOU
35-36 West Newton Street
Schedule

Architects & Associated Designers Inc.
, 96 Congress Street Boston, Massachusetts 02210-1052
Telephone 617-482-7202 Qwip 1200 Telex 951131

78 Measured Drawings

Is the aisle long enough for a rendition of "Here Comes the Bride"? Is the minister's study the right size for spirtual reflection? Is the vestibule sufficiently large? These questions arise when you design a new church. For other buildings, the queries loom just as large. How many arose for Trump Towers in New York City? Or the Transamerica Building in San Francisco?

For all, rehabilitations requiring measured drawing dimensioning is a nail-biting chore. It also is one of the strengths of CAD. Create your own measured drawings on CAD and turn them into schematics. Even in the preliminary stage you are capable of impressing your client with precise detailing of areas. Such knowledge in the preliminary stages requires knowing the general dimensions of a structure. Let CAD calculate the rest. Sit back and let the dimensions appear magically on your screen.

The following example is a measured drawing of the **West Concord Union Church** in Concord, Massachusetts created by Rolland Thompson:

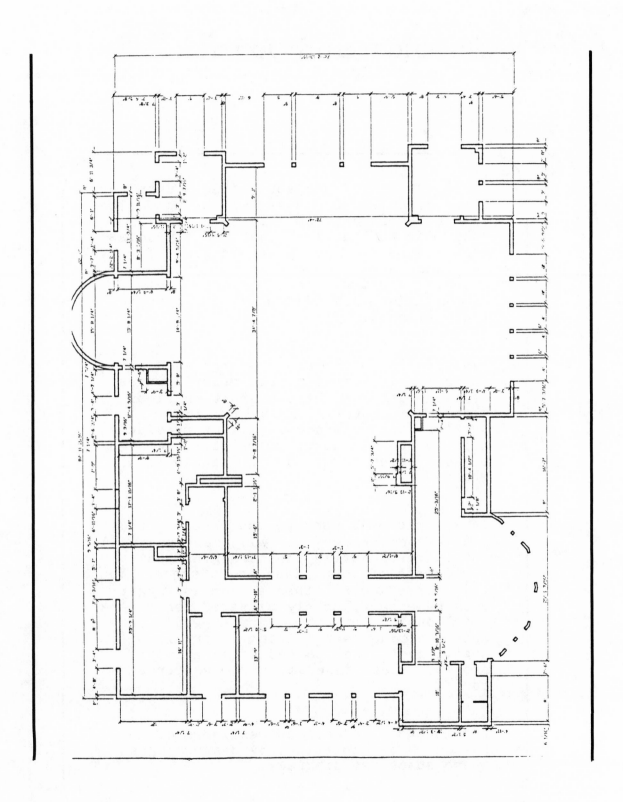

101 Uses For Your A/E Microcomputer   145

79 Bubbles and Arrows

Foresight on A/E projects often determines
their outcome. One useful planning device
is the bubble diagram. It is a simple
schematic of "bubbles" that roughly shows
space layout. They appear to float freely
on paper, anchored to arrows. These
graphic representations allow A/E's to
communicate a simplified graphic form to
their clients.

By labelling each bubble with a room name,
it is possible to indicate relationships
of space use long before starting floor
plans. In addition, by making some
bubbles larger than others, you provide a
quick statement about space size. Arrows
suggest which rooms will be linked to
which.

Take a microCAD package and create your
bubbles and arrows. As you draw, you will
intuitively realize the strengths and
weaknesses of your ideas about space. You
will ferret out whether a room is larger
than necessary, poorly situated, or
functional. The microcomputer will, in a
sense, become part of your internal
juggling of concepts and ideas about a
project. Let it become a soothsayer of
sorts.

Architects & Associated Designers of
Boston, Massachusetts provides a program
phase space-use diagram:

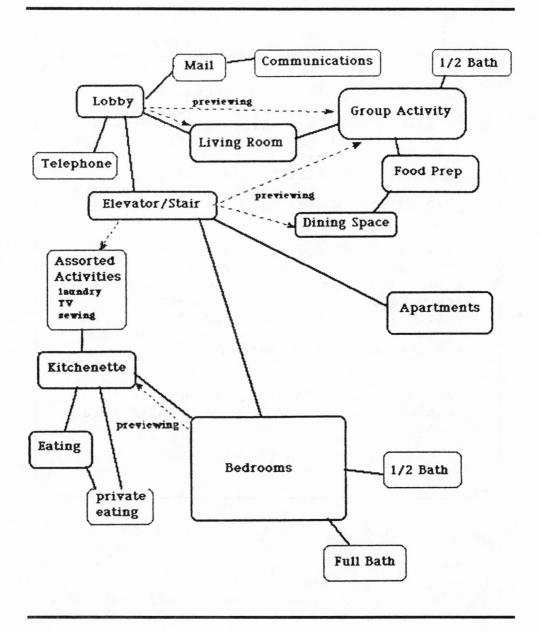

30 Sameness Equals Power

If you are developing a reputation in a
particular building type, consider CAD a
friend. There is nothing as fantastic as
CAD's prototypical space capabilities. It
allows you to keep a good collection of
spaces at your finger tips. So when
clients want to see examples, you can show
them on your monitor right then and there.

In many cases, such a file ferrets out the
likes and dislikes of your clients. You
are also in a position to make your
prejudices known before a project
proceeds. CAD can also prevent
unrealistic expectations from designers
who are becoming too dreamy.

environ inc., a Chicago, Illinois
architecture and design firm created this
example:

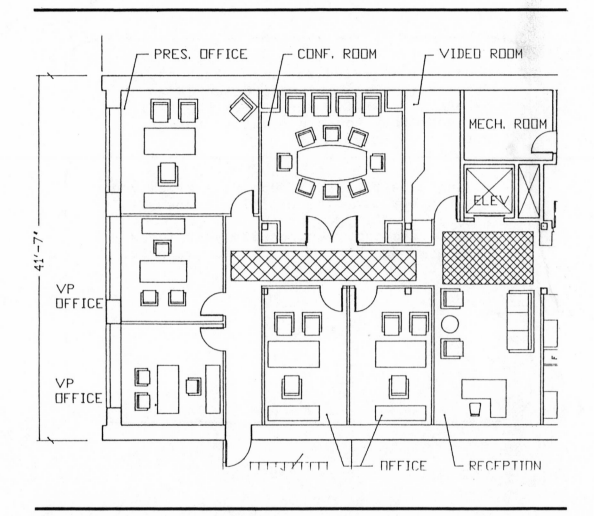

PRES. OFFICE   CONF. ROOM   VIDEO ROOM

MECH. ROOM

ELEV

VP OFFICE

VP OFFICE

OFFICE   RECEPTION

41'-7'

81 Icon Replication

Door swings. Window types. Laboratory
furniture. Each of these deserves an
expertly drawn CAD icon. Develop a file
of icons that you can refer to repeatedly
when you develop a drawing.

Having an established icon file gives you
great power over the drafting process. It
also means that you don't have to redraw
icons. Instead, you perfect your icons
over time and have them at your disposal
for all your projects.

82 Climatic Impact

What direction should a building face?
Is there any way to visualize how the sun
will fall on a building? Is it possible
to know in the schematic design stage -
before you are committed?

The **University of Oregon Department of
Architecture** is using CAD to answer some
of these questions. The department's
effort goes beyond basic use of existing
software, but its initial work can be
simulated for presentation purposes. The
ultimate aim of the project is to "very
quickly determine approximate
performances and make preliminary
decisions about design ideas".

In the accompanying example, supplied by
the University of Oregon, you see two
illustrations. The first is a building
with a window scheme. The second
illustration shows which windows the sun
will pass. Using the shading
capabilities of CAD, develop your own
models based on an understanding of your
climate.

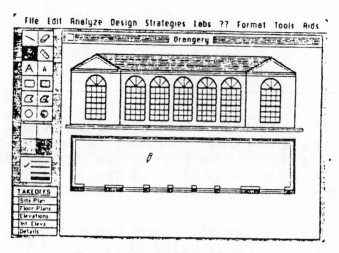

Figure 1. Drawing a Building

These are illustrations of what a user sees on the computer screen when working with our preliminary version of a graphic interface. Figure 1 shows a building being drawn in elevation and plan, with the pallette of drawing tools to the left and a selection of "pull-down menus" across the top. Figure 2 shows the same building in "take-off" mode, where the windows are being measured for solar evaluation. The square outline at the lower right represents the optimum window size and is filled with a grey pattern to match the area of glass which the user has measured. Thus the user can decide whether a building has enough glass for solar heat without leaving the highly graphic, non-numeric drawing mode.

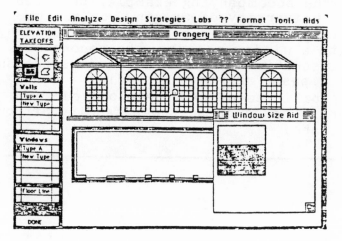

Figure 2. Measuring and evaluating the glass in a buildling

83 The Modular Mode

Ever design an apartment complex where all
Unit A-1 resembled Unit Z-1? You spent
hours on that first unit. After that,
each building was the same except for
direction and placement. Not very
exciting work. But profitable -- and
relatively simple.

Simple, that is if you have CAD. Then you
design Unit A-1, flip it to make B-1 and
flop it to do the rest of the units. This
is one of the major time-saving reasons
why CAD deserves your attention. It does
the repetitive non-creative work in a
snap.

D. C. A. Engineering of Henniker, New
Hampshire supplies the example:

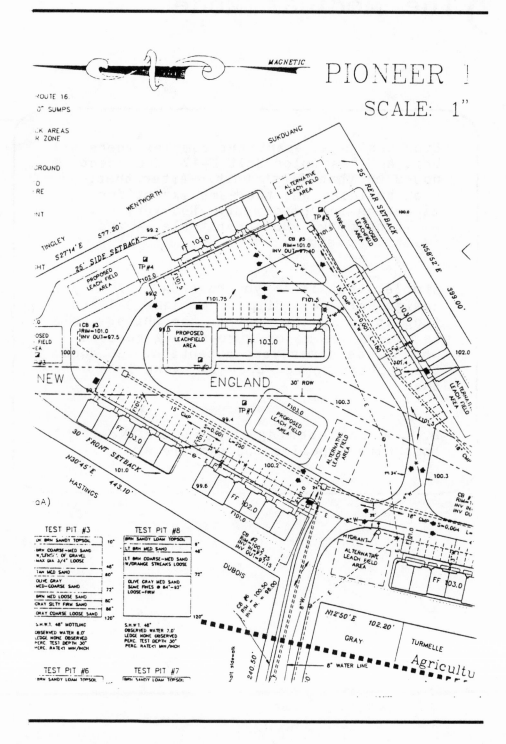

8 4 Extract Info

When you hear "CAD" you immediately
think of graphics. Well . . . that is
one component of CAD. Another -- and
one highly valued by A/E's, is data
extraction. This is the ability of CAD
software in conjunction with basic
database software to create notes and
schedules of information.

Data extraction is quickly making CAD
much more than a drafting tool. This
technique allows A/E's to resource any
kind of nongraphic information on a CAD
drawing. For example, say you are
designing a subdivision with bushes and
need to know the exact number of bushes.
In the past, that required hand counting.
With data extraction, you literally pull
the numbers from the drawings. If you
have measured drawings and you require a
cost estimated per space, you can now
have that information quickily assembled
and ready for analysis. Furthermore, if
you decide to add that information to
your drawings, you merely ask the CAD-
database software -- and, eureka -- notes
appear.

environ inc. of Chicago, Illinois provides
an example of a database extracted from
drawings:

166 WEST WASHINGTON

DOORNO	ROOM NAME	DWIDTH	DHEIGHT	DTYP	DHDW	DRATE	DCONS	DGLASS	DFIN	DTHICK	DFCONS	FFIN	DOOR HEAD	DOOR JAMB	DOOR SILL	DRMRKS
1	EXIT	3-0	7-0	F	1	90MIN	ST	N/A	PG	1-3/4	ST	PG	1	1A	1B	FIRE RATE
2	EXIT	3-0	7-0	F	1	90MIN	ST	N/A	PG	1-3/4	ST	PG	2	2A	2C	RATED
4	MECH. ROOM	2-6	6-8	F	3	60MIN	ST	N/A	PG	1-3/8	ST	PG	2	2A	3A	FIRE DOOR
5	BATH-5	2-8	7-0	F	4	60MIN	WD	N/A	ST	1-3/8	WD	PG	5	5A	5B	HI GLOSS
5	OFFICE-100	2-8	7-0	F	4	60MIN	WD	N/A	ST	1-3/4	ST	PG	5	5A	5B	HI GLOSS
6	VIDEO	2-8	8-0	F	1	60MIN	WD	N/A	ST	1-3/4	ST	PG	6	6A	6B	OAK STAIN
6	OFFICE-177	2-8	8-0	F	1	60MIN	WD	N/A	ST	1-3/4	ST	PG	6	6A	6B	OAK STAIN
6	OFFICE-165	2-8	8-0	F	1	60MIN	WD	N/A	ST	1-3/4	ST	PG	6	6A	6B	OAK STAIN
6	OFFICE-176	2-8	8-0	F	1	60MIN	WD	N/A	ST	1-3/4	ST	PG	6	6A	6B	OAK STAIN
6	OFFICE-156	2-8	8-0	F	1	60MIN	WD	N/A	ST	1-3/4	ST	PG	6	6A	6B	OAK STAIN
6	OFFICE-178	2-8	8-0	F	1	60MIN	WD	N/A	ST	1-3/4	ST	PG	6	6A	6B	OAK STAIN
6	OFFICE-179	2-8	8-0	F	1	60MIN	WD	N/A	ST	1-3/4	ST	PG	6	6A	6B	OAK STAIN

85 Positively Here

Put a locus of a project site on every one
of your drawings. You say "that's a great
idea -- but impractical from a drafting
perspective"? Agreed.

But A/E's know how valuable it is to have
a locus on prints in the field. Why guess
about orientation on project site?

D. C. A. Engineering of Henniker, New
Hampshire puts a locus drawing inside a
box on every one of its major drawings.
The firm specializes in subdivisions and
condominiums, and consequently likes to
lay out the overall picture, since many
structures look similar.

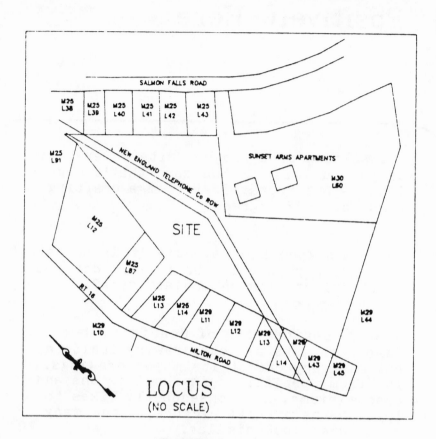

ABUTTERS LIST

Map	Lot	Name
25	38	Nau, Michael E. & Kathleen A., 19 Salmon Falls RD, Rochester NH
25	39	Mailloux Jos. F. & Anita L., 21 Salmon Falls RD, Rochester, NH
25	40	Tingley, Ralph E. & Patricia G., 23 Salmon Falls RD, Rochester, NH
25	41	Wentworth, Paul N. & Patricia G., 25 Salmon Falls RD, Rochester, NH
25	42	Ward, Thomas C. & Traute C., 27 Salmoon Falls RD, Rochester, NH
25	43	Sukduang, Anunta & Patricia A., 29 Salmon Falls RD, Rochester, NH
25	91	Strogen, Robert L. & Diane T., 3 Grove St., Gonic, NH
25	12	Hastings, Richard & Geraldine B., 111 Milton RD, Rochester, NH
25	87	Dubois, Rene L. & Celine, 109 Milton RD, Rochester, NH
25	13	Gray, Arthur K. & Shirley M., 107 Milton RD, Rochester, NH
25	14	Turmelle, Roland & Barbara, 375 Sheridan Ave., Satelite Beach, FL
29	11	Palmer, Edward Geo. Jr. & Fannie E., 22 Frost Hill RD, Eliot, ME
29	12	Paquette, Harold A. & Alberta E., 101 Milton RD, Rochester, NH
29	13	Forcier, Kathleen M., Box 137, Dover NH
29	14	Skalieros, Ekaterini & Vasilios, c/o New England Pizza, 97 Milton RD Rochester, NH
29	43	Fazekas, Joseph & Anna, 47 Portland RD, Rochester, NH
29	44	Fazekas, Joseph & Ervin, 141 Wakefild St. Rochester, NH
29	45	Daudelin, Harold A. & Sharon A., 91 Milton RD, Rochester, NH
29	10	George, Bert D., 151 So. Main St. Rochester, NH
30	60	R & D Realty Trust, P.O. Box 167, Sudbury, MA

86 Title Block It Once

How much time should be dedicated to your drawing identification title blocks? Not much. Enough to list the essentials. How often should you create the blocks? Only once.

But that's impossible, because each project demands a different scale and placement. Again, CAD to the rescue. Create your information block once -- and forever scale and paste it. Never worry about sending a drawing back to the repro shop for alterations. You now control the scaling.

D. C. A. Engineering of Henniker, New Hampshire provides a block example:

PREPARED BY:
    MORRIS C. FOOTE JR.
    D.C.A. ENGINEERING, INC
    FIELD TECH INC.

87 Do It Like Rand McNally

Another essential requirement on every drawing is a graphic scale. It is doubly important in this repro-crazy age of 1/2 size drawings and 8 1/2" X 11" copies. It should be apparent to every drawing user, and yet not so omnipresent that it's distracting. And, graphic scales should be simple -- not so complex that you require a cartographer from Rand McNally around for interpretation.

Find a graphic scale that does the trick. Look at other people's drawings and even at some good maps. Work up yours on CAD, and never do it again. Of course, you will have to change its size for each drawing, but that is a strength of CAD. You can easily edit to change scale from one inch equals 30 feet to one inch equals 100 feet.

D. C. A. Engineering of Henniker, New Hampshire has a simple graphic scale that is standardized for its drawings.

GRAPHIC SCALE

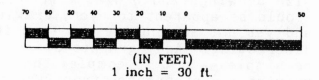

70 60 50 40 30 20 10 0   30

(IN FEET)
1 inch = 30 ft.

REVISIONS		
DESCRIPTION	DRAWN BY: DHB	DATE: 4/2/86
	DWG #: 098603A	JOB NO: 098603
	SCALE: 1" = 30'	SHEET NO. 1 of 1	REV NO:

88 Outlining Drawings

The better your sketchbook is done, the greater its value. For example, it's a precious presentation tool for your client, who could carry it in a briefcase and use it to leverage money from bankers. The same sketchbook could serve as a guide for your drafting crew, so they know exactly what is required of them. That way they won't digest your meager budget too quickly. A sketchbook also helps you -- the author -- since you have at your finger tips a document that shows the overall scheme of a project.

Sure, sure. You've heard this before. Execution is the tough part. Not with CAD. It allows you to fit all of your drawings into an 8 1/2-by-11 inch format. In addition, it makes graphic design relatively easy -- since you can use the same graphics for all your projects. Just remember to save your files.

This example was prepared by Rolland Thompson for a renovation of the **West Concord Union Church** in Concord, Massachussetts:

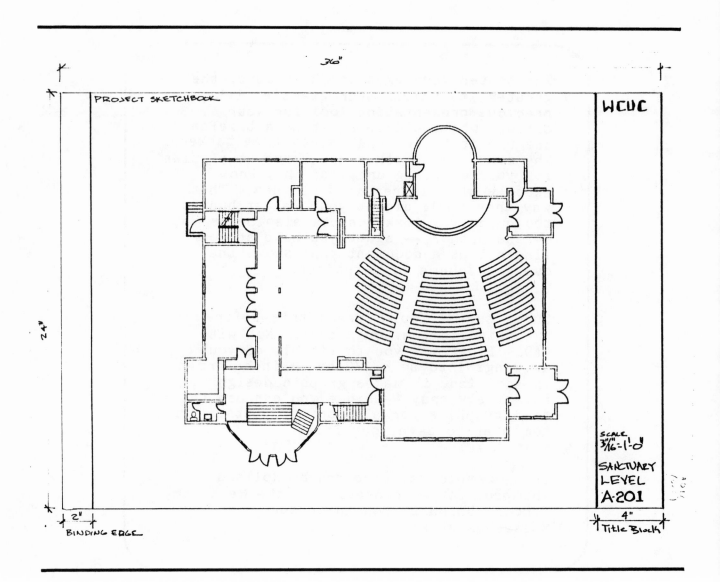

36"

PROJECT SKETCHBOOK

WCUC

24"

SCALE
3"/16=1'-0"

SANCTUARY
LEVEL
A·201

2"
BINDING EDGE

4"
Title Block

89 2,000 Copies From One

How many times have you drafted a window on an elevation manually? Enough to drive you crazy. Wouldn't it have been easier to create it once and never do it again?

The problem is, until CAD you had no choice. If a building had 2,000 windows, you had to draft 2,000 windows. Of course you copied the first one. But still, you had to pencil each one. With CAD, it's designed once and filed on computer memory. In the future, you call it up from the file and alter dimensions and electronically paste it to a drawing.

And the same goes for the detail through the head of this window. Clone a copy from your files, modify it to suit your new design, and your detailing speeds up. Maybe your file copy can be used as is.

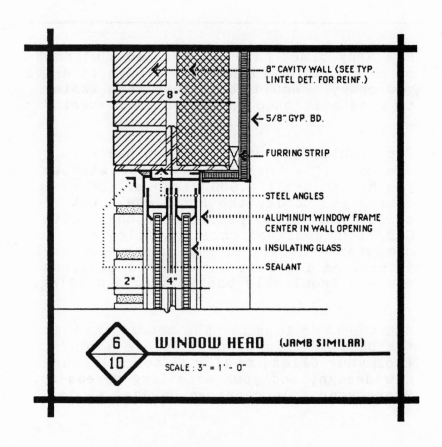

8" CAVITY WALL (SEE TYP. LINTEL DET. FOR REINF.)

8"

5/8" GYP. BD.

FURRING STRIP

STEEL ANGLES

ALUMINUM WINDOW FRAME CENTER IN WALL OPENING

INSULATING GLASS

SEALANT

2" 4"

6/10 WINDOW HEAD (JAMB SIMILAR)

SCALE : 3" = 1' - 0"

Enclosure with October, 1985 issue of
A/E SYSTEMS REPORT, P.O. Box 11316,
Newington, CT 06111.

90 Legend Development

When you first conquer the basics of CAD, you are in position to develop your materials legend. Everybody seems to have separate ideas about materials legend. CAD provides you with the freedom to experiment since it is so easy to edit.

Developing a materials legend should get close scrutiny and become an office standard. When developing this and other legends, consider the opportunity to change scale and definitions for each drawing.

91 Wordsmithing

Writing general notes is not a delight. First, they demand succinct and accurate phrasing. Notes should enhance a drawing -- not complicate it. Second, general notes require excellent lettering capabilities. Sloppy notes on a major project is inexcusable. Third, they should be scaled relative to their importance. Since drawings change throughout a project, their building notes may change proportionately.

The authors suggest you let CAD do your writing. Inherent to CAD is a basic word processing capability. Though not very sophisticated as yet, it is becoming so. One of its best attributes is scaling. It happens on command and requires no major alternation.

D. C. A. Engineering of Henniker, New Hampshire offers the accompanying example:

(Authors' Note: Always keep text to a minimum. Save writing for the specifications.)

NOTES:

1. PROPOSED USE OF THE PROPERTY IS FOR 48
   2 BEDROOM TOWNHOUSE UNITS.

2. OWNER OF THE RECORD IS PIONEER REALTY
   & INVESTMENT TRUST.

3. PARKING REQ'D = 1.5 SPACES/UNIT.
   PARKING PROVIDED = 2.5 SPACES/UNIT.

4. SEWAGE WILL BE DISPOSED OF ON-SITE
   IN CONVENTIONAL LEACH FIELDS.

5. PARKING SETBACKS: FRONT = 30 ft.
                       REAR & SIDE = 20 ft.

6. BUILDING SETBACKS: FRONT = 30 ft.
                        REAR & SIDE = 25 ft.

7. AREA OF PARCEL = 11.3 ACRES.

8. WATER TO BE SUPPLIED FROM MUNICIPAL MAIN ON ROUTE 16.

9. CATCH BASINS TO BE PRECAST CONCRETE WITH 2'-0" SUMPS
   AND TYPE "B" GRATES

10. TREES & NATURAL VEGETATION IN BUILDING SETBACK AREAS
    ARE TO BE MAINTAINED AS A GREEN SPACE BUFFER ZONE

11. PARKING SPACES TO BE 9'x 20' (TYPICAL)

12. ELECTRIC & TELEPHONE LINES TO BE RUN ABOVE GROUND

13. THE ENTRANCE TO THE PROJECT IS TO BE BUILT TO
    TOWN SPECIFICATIONS FROM MILTON ROAD TO WHERE
    THE ROAD FLARES (±300 ft.)

14. ASPHALT SIDEWALKS ARE TO BE INSTALLED INFRONT
    OF ALL BUILDINGS AS SHOWN ON PLAN

15. ALL ACCESS WAYS AND PARKING AREAS
    WILL HAVE ASPHALT CURBING

16. ALL UNITS TO HAVE AN EXTERIOR POLE LIGHT
    LOCATED AT END OF WALKWAY AND ATTACHED LIGHT
    AT EACH DOOR ENTRANCE

92 Arrows and Symbols

Engineers think in symbols. Their drawings are more symbolic than an architect's. An "O" with two vertical lines through it does not look like a convenience outlet. But that's what it is according to an engineer's way of thinking.

D. C. A. Engineering in Henniker, New Hampshire is responsible for the example. The firm has symbols for drainage arrows, existing spot elevations, finish floor elevations, existing contour lines, finish contour lines, water lines, electrical lines, power poles, gate valves, dumpster locations and traffic flow arrows.

LEGEND

——▸	DRAINAGE FLOW ARROWS
100.0	EXISTING SPOT ELEVATIONS
F100.0	FINISH SPOT ELEVATIONS
FF 100.0	FINISH FLOOR ELEVATIONS
– – –	EXISTING CONTOUR LINES
———	FINISH CONTOUR LINES
— W —	WATER LINE
—— E —	ELECTRIC LINE
O	POWER POLE
⋈	GATE VALVE
■	DUMPSTER LOCATION
◀	TRAFFIC FLOW ARROWS

93 Details, Details, Details

Take advantage of CAD for engineering drawings full of detail specifications. That's another beautiful aspect of CAD. Since you spent hours calculating specifications for a wall or a roof, it only makes sense to keep all of that information with your drawing.

Collaborative Design Group of Tucson, Arizona used CAD to create the detail of a retaining wall at an apartment complex. They now have the ability to plot as many of these complicated drawings as they need. And, at a later date, should one of those many specifications change, they can make this one change, rather create another drawing.

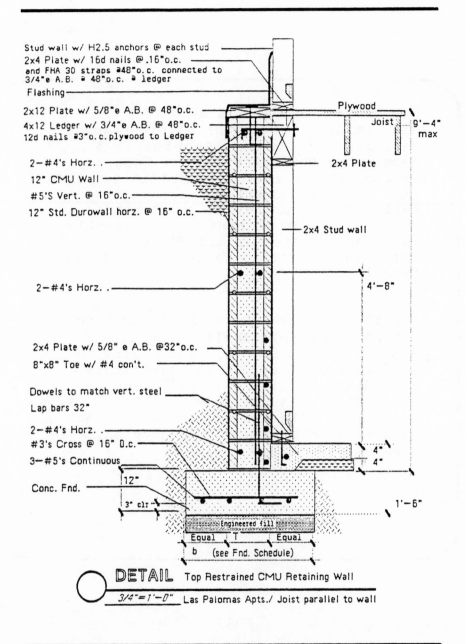

Stud wall w/ H2.5 anchors @ each stud
2x4 Plate w/ 16d nails @ .16"o.c.
and FHA 30 straps @48"o.c. connected to
3/4"∅ A.B. @ 48"o.c. @ ledger
Flashing

2x12 Plate w/ 5/8"∅ A.B. @ 48"o.c.
4x12 Ledger w/ 3/4"∅ A.B. @ 48"o.c.
12d nails @3"o.c.plywood to Ledger

2-#4's Horz. .
12" CMU Wall
#5'S Vert. @ 16"o.c.
12" Std. Durowall horz. @ 16" o.c.

2-#4's Horz. .

2x4 Plate w/ 5/8" ∅ A.B. @32"o.c.
8"x8" Toe w/ #4 con't.

Dowels to match vert. steel
Lap bars 32"

2-#4's Horz. .
#3's Cross @ 16" O.c.
3-#5's Continuous

Conc. Fnd.

Plywood
Joist   9'-4" max

2x4 Plate

2x4 Stud wall

4'-8"

4"
4"

1'-6"

12"
3" clr

Engineered fill

Equal   T   Equal
b   (see Fnd. Schedule)

⊙ DETAIL Top Restrained CMU Retaining Wall
3/4"=1'-0" Las Palomas Apts./ Joist parallel to wall

94 Recalling Details

CAD has no bounds. It does not discriminate between classification of details. For example, **Architects & Associated Designers Inc.** of Boston creates and files its isometric details on CAD. Isometrics are valuable for designers in portraying construction details and for mechanics who assemble parts of a system in the field. An important isometric application is roofing detail.

Architects & Associated Designers Inc. offers an example shelf-angle detail. Since the firm is small and trying to economize on time, it has saved this detail and will call it back from its computer memory for other jobs. Or, it will modify the design for another job and update for revision of the original drawing.

Architects & Associated Designers Inc./A&AD
286 Congress Street Boston, Massachusetts 02210-1052
Telephone 617 482 7502   Qwip 1200   Telex 951131

Date.................... Proj. No..........................

Project:...

Dwg. Title...

Dwg. No............ Scale...

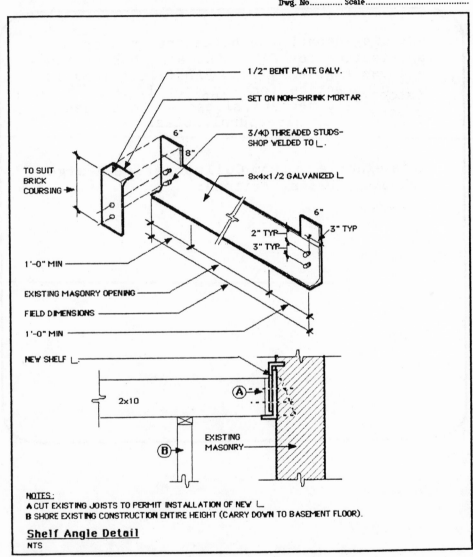

1/2" BENT PLATE GALV.

SET ON NON-SHRINK MORTAR

3/4Ø THREADED STUDS-
SHOP WELDED TO ∟.

8×4×1/2 GALVANIZED ∟

TO SUIT
BRICK
COURSING

6"

8"

6"

3" TYP

2" TYP

3" TYP

1'-0" MIN

EXISTING MASONRY OPENING

FIELD DIMENSIONS

1'-0" MIN

NEW SHELF ∟

2×10

Ⓐ

Ⓑ

EXISTING
MASONRY

NOTES:
A CUT EXISTING JOISTS TO PERMIT INSTALLATION OF NEW ∟
B SHORE EXISTING CONSTRUCTION ENTIRE HEIGHT (CARRY DOWN TO BASEMENT FLOOR).

Shelf Angle Detail
NTS

95 Description & Notes

Building department notes are another application for CAD. Put all those notes you use regularly in a CAD file. This is a good practice for structural, electrical, mechanical and -- to a lesser extent -- architectural notes.

This example is from **Collaborative Design Group** of Tucson, Arizona:

JOB SPECIFIC FOUNDATION SCHEDULE

NOTES_____

FOUNDATION SCHEDULE NOTES

SLABS ON GRADE

CONCRETE SLABS: SECTION 03050
==

SEE FOUNDATION PLAN FOR LOCATIONS

THICKNESS: 4 Inches
SUBBASE: 4 Inches River Run
Fill
REINFORCING: None
EXPANSION STRIPS: 1/2" Fiber at
Stems Typical
CONSTRUCTION JOINTS: See Plan

SLAB: S-1

FOOTINGS

CONCRETE: SECTION 03050
==

NOTE: ALL FOOTING EXCAVATIONS SHALL BE INTO NATURAL
MATERIALS OR ENGINEERED FILL AS DESCRIBED IN SOILS
ENGINEERS, SOILS INVESTIGATION REPORT.
     : DEPTH OF FOOTINGS SHALL FOLLOW RECOMMENDATIONS
OF SOILS ENGINEERS, SOILS INVESTIGATION REPORT.

STEM WALLS

CONCRETE MASONRY UNITS: SECTION 04220
CONCRETE: SECTION 03050
==

ALL MASONRY CELLS GROUTED TYPICAL

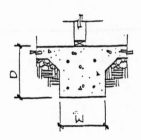

TYPE: CONTINUOUS MONOLITHIC
LOCATION: FRAME BEARING WALLS
DETAIL REFERENCE:_____

FOOTER:
 SIZE: 16 INCHES WIDE X 18
 INCHES DEEP
 REINFORCING:
  HORIZONTAL: 2-#4 CONTINUOUS
  TOP AND BOTTOM
 VERTICAL:
   NONE
   EMBEDMENTS: NONE

FOOTING: #F-1

96 Automatic Manual

Combine data and graphics into an elaborate, aesthetically pleasing office manual. You will have the power to control dimensions of text and provide strong illustration to back up points.

Designing an office manual with CAD is an excellent and effective way to learn how to use computers. You really shouldn't worry about generating text. You should, instead, paste your word processor-produced text, mixing it with CAD graphics. Graphics could be as simple as borders around a page. This is a good in-house use.

Todd Lee/FR Clark & Associates provide the following dimensioning example:

CADD DIMENSIONING PROCEDURES

1. Use —⚡— 45 degree slash to indicate limits of dimensions.

2. Dimension from Reference Points as required by design:

      From Grid Line:

      From ℄   of: Structure
                of: Wall, partition, etc.

      From Face of: Structural Element
                 of: Finished Surface

3. Do not close dimensions of interior strings unless necessary, in which case indicate adjustable or float dimension with +/- sign.

   4.   Use   dot to indicate limits of modular dimensions.

   5.   For manual drafting, elimijnate feet and inches symboles and show
        dimensions as follows: 6 feet 0 inches   6-0
                                 4 feet 11 inches   4-11
                                 3 feet 6 1/2 inches   3-6 1/2
                                 10 1/4 inches   10 1/4
                                 1 foot   1-0 (not "12")

   6.   For CADD, we will use program that has feet (') and inch (")
        symbols until we develop automatic dimensioning program that
        eliminates such symbols. (Note: it will simplify drawing, reduce
        plotting time, and make 1/2 size prints more readable).

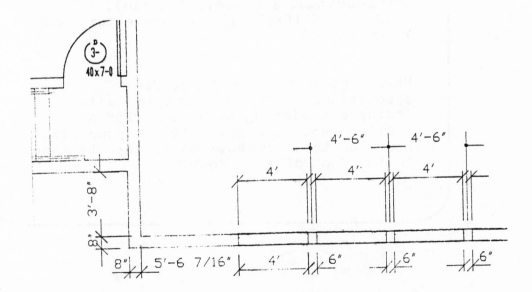

Todd Lee/FR Clark Associates, Inc.27 - 27   05-20-1986

97 Listing Visuals

Use CAD to make an eyecatching punchlist that is graphically correct. For your CAD database, prepare individual room layouts for each space in your client's project. Then print each room on an 8 1/2x11-inch customized form that also contains a list of generic CAD symbols.

For example: C (Clean), F (Furnish/Install), M (Missing), P (Paint) and R (Repair). On the same page, include the line item for the finish schedule of each room. List each item numerically, 1 (Flooring), 2 (Base), 3 (Dado), 4 (Wall), 5 (Ceiling), 6 (Convector) and 7 (Built-in).

Having these symbols simplifies annotation. "2M", for example, will indicate a missing base, and "P5" a ceiling requiring painting. A punchlist based on these symbols could then be taped to the door of each room.

98 Organize Your Space

Facilities management is getting top billing as a CAD application. Many FM functions are eased with CAD. That is not to say all. Some require non-graphic systems. Others a combination.

Computer Controls Corp., an HVAC systems manufacturer in Wilmington, Massachusetts, uses CAD in-house for organizing and maintaining its work spaces (slowly being referred to as "workstations" regardless of whether a computer terminal is present or not). In the accompanying CAD drawing, a small CAD work space is rearranged for maximum space and utility.

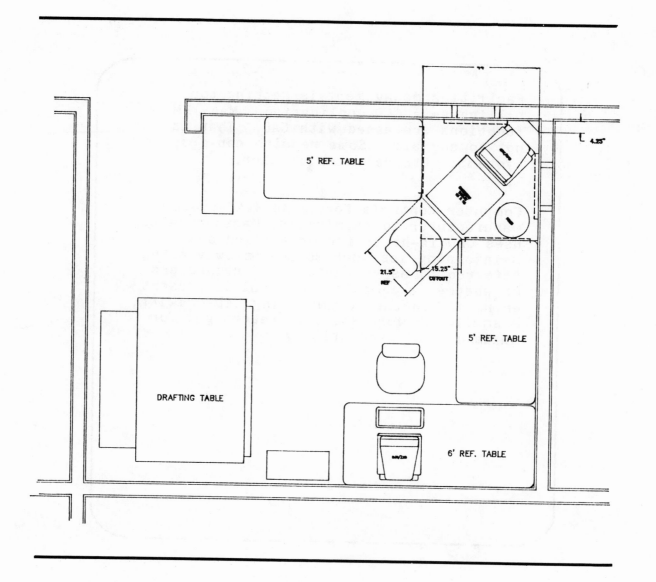

5' REF. TABLE

4.25"

21.5"
REF

15.25"
CUTOUT

5' REF. TABLE

DRAFTING TABLE

6' REF. TABLE

101 Uses For Your A/E Microcomputer

Everyday uses for the microcomputer are not limited to software. Microcomputer hardware also provides very practical alternatives. This section examines networking and keyboard functions that will demonstrate the versatility of microcomputers.

Networking is the connection of computers. It allows computers in your office or in other locations to work together or borrow from each other's memories. The networking example in this section demonstrates how to collect information from a large commercial database. By hooking a microcomputer to a database via a telephone, it is possible to access hundreds of specialized scientific and engineering databases throughout the world.

This access is possible via a "modem," a device that allows microcomputers and the telephone system to communicate numbers, graphics and text. As a result, A/E's do not have to send away for specialized information or travel to libraries. Instead, they can turn to their microcomputer and collect information from databases, from the latest on water drainage to ratings of materials.

Another example looks at the "print-screen" function on a microcomputer keyboard. This function makes it possible to print exactly what is on a screen. It is an attribute of microcomputers that opens many avenues. For instance, it will allow you to print out "help" instructions that are imbedded in software. A collection of these instructions constitutes an operating manual. But that is only the beginning. This print-screen function allow you to produce hardcopy quickly without spending time formating.

99 Owner's $ Status

A/E clients need to track hard and soft costs on a project. They have to keep track of architects' fees and prices of furniture and furnishings. Any change in construction also translates into additional costs.

During renovation of the Old South Church of Boston, Massachusetts, the accompanying example was used to help church officials remain aware of costs throughout the project. Since the renovations were major, church officials worried about escalating costs and possible budget overruns.

They received a weekly printout during construction like the example.
It helped the officials maximize the aesthetics of the project, while controlling the cost of the renovation. During each phase of the project, the church was in a position to make informed financial decisions about stained glass added scope and other expensive items.

ITEM#	AUTHRZE	CURRENT	CHANGE	CO	DESCRIPTION	ACTION BY	COMMENT
CATEGORY C:					SUBCONTRACTORS AND VENDORS		
C 25.n	0	2769	2769	06	Under Stairs + music lights		
C 26	28500	28500	0	yy	Sound		
C 26.a	1500	1500	0	yy	Alt. #1 hearing impaired		
C 26.b	1500	2856	1356	02	Wiring for recording mikes		
C 26.c	0	1432	1432	02	Junction boxes, conduit		
C 26.d	0	264	264	02	Exchange 2 Electro speakers for Bozak		
C 26.e	0	2916	2916	02	6 AKG 451EB Microphones + A-51 swivels		
C 26.f	0	7132	7132	02	Genie Lift for relamping *		
C 26.g	0	316	316	03	Restocking Charge on revised dimmer		
C 26.h	0	855	855	04	Double sound jacks, add 2 outlets $810		
C 26.i	0	625	625	06	Correction to 26.c"junction boxes,cond"		
C 26.j	0	264	264	06	Additional Choir Room Receptacles		
C 26.k	0	3400	3400	06	Assembly of eight chandeliers		
C 26.1	0	400	400	06	2nd Adjustment of Rambusch Light Baffle		
C 26.m	0	-2474	-2474	xx	Additional electrical GMP Adjustment		
SUBTOT:	636119	699881	63762				
CATEGORY D:					ADD-ONS		
D 27	59590	59590	0	yy	Contractor's Fees * 5 1/2%		
D 28	10834	8735	-2099	05	Permits * 1%, item complete		
D 29	0	0	0	yy	Bond * not wanted		
D 30	32504	0	-32504	yy	Contingency * 3% (Total add-on 9 1/2%)		
SUBTOT:	102928	68325	-34603				
CATEGORY E:					GLASS ESTIMATE		
E 15.a	52980	55340	2360	05	Exterior Glass - GMP		
E 15.b	21690	17356	-4334	xx	Staging		
E 15.c	7094	3062	-4032	xx	Fees, etc. 5 1/2 %		
E 15.d	37616	37616	0	yy	Interior Glass - GMP		
E 15.e	30093	26487	-3606	xx	Staging		
E 15.f	0	1857	1857	02	Switch Balcony Windows		
E 15.g	0	0	0	yy	Lantern glass (see 12.g) within GMP		
E 15.h	6432	3526	-2906	xx	Fees etc. 5 1/2%		
E 15.i	0	633	633	02	Alpha & Omega plastic storm windows		
SUBTOT:	155905	145877	-10028				
CATEGORY F:					OWNER'S CONTINGENCY		
F 30	25000	23558	-1442	05	Repair Roof and Ext Masonry		
F 30.b	0	0	0	yy	Repair Exterior Masonry		Included in F30 adjustment
F 30.c	C	3587	3587	02	Copper clips for heating cable *		
F 30.d	0	2771	2771	06	New downspout at omega, repair NE Vest.		
F 31	5000	0	-5000	04	Repair Sanctuary Piers * not needed		
F 32	5000	4746	-254	02	Repair, Repaint Lantern Ext.		
F 33	2000	3360	1360	02	Fastening for Organ Pipes		
F 34	3000	3000	0	06	Stencil Bombarde/Violone		
F 35	2000	6000	4000	xx	20 Flourescents for Organs/guesstimate		
F 36.a	18000	8018	-9982	03	E.Wall Painting + Stenciling		
F 36.b	2000	1266	-734	03	Clean E.Wall Woodwork+screen		

PAGE 3

100 In-house Technical Manual

Consider your microcomputer a technical manual writer. How often have you flipped through the "help" functions only to return to revive your memory? It's a time-consuming and distracting way to learn how to operate your spreadsheet, word processor or database.

Here's a solution. Use the print screen function to print all your "help" text, directories, formats and any other text that instructs. You can now create your own book of instructions, database field names, etc. You should make this habit second nature.

This practice becomes particularly valuable if you have a harddisk. Periodically, you should print out your directories to delete old ones. Harddisks are efficient when not clogged with too many files. You can also use the print screen capabilities to develop an in-house technial manual. This manual will help orient new employees who are unfamiliar with your microcomputer software.

Rolland Thompson offers the example:

(Authors' Note: Check your operating manual to understand how to use your "print screen" key or keys.)

```
C>date
Current date is Tue  1-01-1980
Enter new date (mm-dd-yy): 05-27-1986

C>time
Current time is  0:00:37.03
Enter new time: 08:06

C>path=c:\dos;c:\

C>prompt $p$g

C:\>
C:\>dir


 Volume in drive C has no label
 Directory of  C:\

SIT      COM       788    1-01-80   9:28a
AUTOEXEC BAT        43    5-12-86   9:53a
CONFIG   SYS        23    5-12-86   9:54a
DBASE3       <DIR>         5-08-86   4:51p
VW           <DIR>         5-08-86   4:52p
DBASE2       <DIR>         5-08-86   4:52p
15PERINC            13    7-09-84   9:29a
HELP     VW      11779    7-24-83   1:18p
COMMAND  COM     23210    9-30-85  12:00p
INSTALL  BAT        75    7-24-83   1:18p
DOS          <DIR>         1-01-80  12:00a
        11 File(s)   9076736 bytes free

C:\>copy 15perinc prn:

        1 File(s) copied

C:\>dir a:

 Volume in drive A has no label
 Directory of  A:\

CONFIG   SYS       91    2-09-86   3:59a
WORKLIST FRM     1990    5-12-86  12:13p
AUTOEXEC BAT       60    1-01-80   2:33a
NEWMAIL3 DEF   222208    1-01-80   6:01a
AUTOEXEC BAK       60    1-01-80   2:27a
15PERINC           13    7-09-84   9:29a
LASTNAME NDX    35328    1-01-80   6:01a
ADDLIST3 FRM     1990   12-20-85  11:55a
TODDFORM FRM     1990    1-01-80  12:44a
ADDLIST1 FRM     1990    1-20-86  12:24p
ADDLIST5 FRM     1990    5-12-86  12:06p
POSTERS  LBL     1034    1-01-80   1:38a
        12 File(s)    88064 bytes free

C:\>cd c:\dbase3

C:\DBASE3>dbase

. set defa to a
```

101 On-line Librarian

The local university or public library used to be the place to do project research. No longer! Now it's not necessary to leave your office. Turn on your microcomputer, dial a telephone number, and access information on hundreds of databases. Collect references and even full manuscripts. It may cost more than going to the local university, but it's more reliable, more thorough and reaps rewards much quicker and cheaper.

Engineers at **J. Kenneth Fraser and Associates** of Rensselaer, New York formerly used the library at Rensselaer Polytechnic Institute in nearby Troy, New York. Recently, they installed a modem and communications software in their microcomputer. When the firm required information on communication control for a municipal water distribution system, they gleaned the information from the WATERNET database. Here is an example of a database session:

SUBJECT COVERAGE

o drinking water industry
o water reuse and wastewater reuse
o industrial water use
o water renovation and recycling
o toxicological and medical related
   data
o health effects and environmental
   problems
o financing, management, and
   administration

o automated process control
o water quality and treatment
o law and water
o water pollution
o water resources
o energy costs and treated water
o training materials
o history of water supply
o water rates and water conservation

SOURCES

WATERNET contains abstracts of the Journal AWWA, AWWA's Annual Conference
Proceedings, Water Quality Technology Conference Proceedings, Distribution
System Symposium Proceedings, all AWWA Conference Seminars since 1967, AWWARF
Water Quality Research Newsletter, and wastewater reuse and potable reuse
information.

ORIGIN

WATERNET is produced by the American Water Works Association. Questions
concerning file content should be directed to:

Kurt Keeley   Telephone: 303/794-7711
Technical Information Services Manager
American Water Works Association
6666 W. Quincy Ave.
Denver, CO 80235

FILE FORMAT

[#] 004627   [an] jaw77159
[ti] toxicology and drinking water contaminants
[au] stokinger, herbert e.;
[pu] publ: awwa
[jn] journal american water works association, p 399-402 , july [py] 1977,
[co] coden: jawwa5 issn [sn] 0003-150x
[av] source: awwa
     27 references, tables, figures
[la] languages: english
[dt] doc type: jnl article
[ab] evidence is presented to support the concept of response thresholds for
     toxic...toward error in extrapolating animal data to humans.
[de] descriptors: chloroform;
[sc] subject codes: 4300; 0300;

[#] dialog accession number   [an] awwa accession#
[ti] title   [au] author
[pu] publisher   [jn] journal name
[py] publication yr   [co] coden
[sn] intl std s/n   [av] availability
[la] language   [dt] document type
[ab] abstract   [de] descriptor

Authors

Daniel S. Raker

Daniel S. Raker is president of Design & Systems Research, Inc., a Cambridge, Massachusetts-based management consulting firm specializing in computer graphics applications and market research. He also is founder of The MicroCAD Institute, a professional computer-aided design training center in Cambridge.

Mr. Raker is editor of the **A/E SYSTEMS REPORT**, a leading monthly newsletter on automation and reprographics in professional design organizations. In addition to the newsletter, Mr. Raker's column "CAD Angles" appears monthly in Plan and Print magazine.

Mr. Raker is an avid writer and educator in the field of computer graphics. Mr. Raker developed and taught the first full course on CADD at the Harvard Graduate School of Design. Recently, he has delivered dozens of presentations and authored articles under the auspices of the AIA, the National Design Engineering Conference, the National Computer Graphics Association, Computer Aided Engineering, and the International Reprographics Association.

In addition, Mr. Raker is the author of two books on microcomputer-based CADD named **The Microcomputer CAD Manual** and **INSIDE AutoCAD.**

Mr. Raker's experience in computer graphics comes from General Telephone and Electronics (GTE) Laboratories where he worked as an assistant research director, and from the Harvard University Laboratory for Computer Graphics where he held the position of Director of Services and was responsible for applications development, and graphics education and training. Mr. Raker earned his Bachelor of Arts degree from Harvard College.

Rolland D. Thompson, FAIA

Rolland D. Thompson comes to DSR with 32 years of
architectural practice as a designer and principal
in the firms of Steinhardt & Thompson and Gruzen and
Partners in New York, and is now associated with
Todd Lee/FR Clark Associates, Inc.

He has taught professional practice and management at
the Harvard Graduate School of Design and the City
University of New York, and occasionally teaches
continuing education courses at the Harvard Graduate
School of Design.

Mr. Thompson has been an enthusiastic practitioner of
overlay drafting for many years, and now combines his
experience in this technique with computer-aided
drafting and design. He also has extensive experience
in word processing, spreadsheets and database
applications.

His book, **Production Technology for Architects and
Engineers**, will be published late this year by John
Wiley & Sons. Mr. Thompson has also begun writing a
book entitled **Graphic Retrieval and Reference/Standard
Details**. Both of these books advise architects on
efficient ways of producing contract documents quickly
and with quality control. They include creative ways
of using manual data processing and computer graphics
methods.

Design & Systems Research Publishing Co. Inc. is a publisher of books and newsletters about technology for design professionals in architecture and engineering. Its products offer an indepth look at how design professionals should apply technology in their work. The company's productions do not seek to promote any one product but rather to discuss how to use the products as a class of technological tools.

DESIGN & SYSTEMS RESEARCH inc.

Name _____

Shipping_____
Address
        _____

        _____

Phone (____) _____

Book Order Form

Mail To:

Design & Systems Research
P.O. Box 1022
Cambridge MA 02140-1022

Quantity	Book	Price	Total
_____	**101 Uses For Your A/E Microcomputer** 24.95 by Dan Raker and Rolland Thompson Practical Ideas for Everyday Situations in Architectural and Engineering Firms. Use the word processor, database, and spreadsheet program you already have. 208 pages. Published by Design & Systems Research Publishing Company, 1986. ISBN 0-934605-00-9		_____
_____	**INSIDE AutoCAD** 27.95 by Dan Raker and Harbert Rice A Software Teaching Guide and Handbook that gives you information you need to know about AutoCAD, the most popular microcomputer drafting and design program. 320 pages. Published by New Riders Publishing, 1985. ISBN 0-934035-03-2		_____
_____	**The Microcomputer CAD Manual** 27.95 by Harbert Rice and Dan Raker A Complete Guide to Selecting and Implementing a Micro-CAD System. 240 pages. Published by New Riders Publishing, 1986. ISBN 0-934035-04-0		_____

Subtotal   _____
Mass. res. add 5% sales tax   _____
Shipping, First Book $3.50
Shipping, $1.00 each addit.   _____
Total   _____

Payment   Card Number _____

[ ] Check   Expiration date _____   MC Interbank # _____
[ ] MasterCard
[ ] Visa   Signature _____

125 CambridgePark Drive Cambridge, Massachusetts 02140 Telephone: (617) 497-5300